LIMITS

The Concept and Its
Role in Mathematics

A BLAISDELL SCIENTIFIC PAPERBACK

in the School Mathematics Series

ROBERT E. K. ROURKE, *Saint Stephen's School, Rome*

CONSULTING EDITOR

LIMITS | The Concept and Its Role in Mathematics

AN INTRODUCTORY TREATMENT

NORMAN MILLER

BLAISDELL PUBLISHING COMPANY

A Division of Ginn and Company

NEW YORK · TORONTO · LONDON

Preface

This exposition of the role of limits in mathematics is intended for the use, mainly, of teachers and students in high schools. It is not intended for mathematicians who require a compact treatment of the subject. There is no lack of such treatments in the literature.

The necessary preliminary mathematics, given in Chapter II, can be omitted by readers who are already familiar with the ideas presented. The last three chapters are designed to open doors to the three main applications of limits: infinite series, the derivative, and the definite integral. In each of these chapters, only enough material is presented to exhibit and illustrate the role of limits in the subject. The four appendices are intended for readers whose curiosity has been aroused regarding the topics discussed.

The two objectives that I have striven for are accuracy and readability. In line with the second of these objectives, I have not hesitated to enlarge on some points even at the risk of prolixity or to wander into byways if they seemed to add interest to the subject. The main theorems are plentifully illustrated by examples. Sets of exercises are provided for the use of students and teachers.

It is hoped that, from a study of this book, readers will acquire an appreciation of the vital role of limits in mathematics and a curiosity regarding their further development.

It is a pleasure to express my gratitude to Mr. R. E. K. Rourke, who read the first draft of the manuscript and made many useful suggestions.

N. M.

Contents

LIMITS | The Concept and Its Role in Mathematics

Chapter I | Introduction

1.1 Historical Introduction

The word *limit* shares with the words *set, variable,* and *function,* which are discussed in Chapter II, the characteristic of being in common use in our speech. Like these also, its meaning must be narrowed and sharply defined in order that it fill a useful role in mathematics. Since the middle of the seventeenth century, the concept of limit has been one of the fundamental ideas in mathematics. Its origins, however, go back much farther. The ancient Greeks, with their penchant for logic, struggled long to come to terms with the notion of limits.

The paradoxes of *Zeno* (495–435 B.C.) formed a tantalizing challenge to the Greek world of the fifth century B.C. Of these the best known is that of the mythical race between Achilles and the tortoise. If Achilles can run ten times as fast as the tortoise, which began the race with a 100-yard head start, then everyone knew that Achilles would overtake the tortoise. The trouble was to dispose of the "proof" of Zeno that the tortoise would always be ahead. Zeno's argument was as follows: while Achilles is covering the 100 yards between their starting points, the tortoise moves ahead 10 yards; while Achilles races over this 10 yards, the tortoise plods on 1 yard and is still 1 yard ahead; when Achilles has covered this 1 yard, the tortoise is still $\frac{1}{10}$ of a yard ahead. So, by dividing the distance run by Achilles into intervals of 100, 10, 1, $\frac{1}{10}$, $\frac{1}{100}$, and so on, yards, Zeno argued that Achilles would never pass the tortoise. The fact that an infinite set of distances could add up to a finite, indeed a fairly short, total distance was the stumbling block that required a doctrine of limits to remove.

The paradoxes were not the only assault made by the Greeks on the fortress of limits. Two of their greatest mathematicians,

1

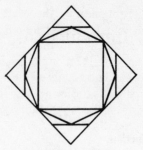

Figure   1.1

Eudoxus (408–355 B.C.) and *Archimedes* (287–212 B.C.) calculated lengths, areas, and volumes by a limiting process that came to be known as the *Method of Exhaustions*. In the hands of Archimedes, this became a powerful tool. It is illustrated by the following example.

Suppose we wish to find the length of a circle with a given radius. In this circle, inscribe a square and about it circumscribe another square. It seems reasonably certain that the length of the circle lies between the perimeters of the two squares. If the squares are replaced by inscribed and circumscribed regular octagons, as shown in Figure 1.1 the perimeters of these octagons approximate more closely to the length of the circle. By increasing the number of sides, taking regular polygons of 16, 32, 64, . . . sides, we can make the perimeters of the two inscribed and circumscribed polygons differ by as little as we wish. By this means Archimedes found that the value of π lies between $3\frac{1}{7}$ and $3\frac{10}{71}$.

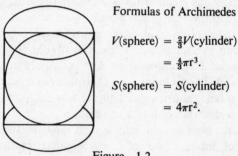

Formulas of Archimedes

$$V(\text{sphere}) = \tfrac{2}{3}V(\text{cylinder})$$
$$= \tfrac{4}{3}\pi r^3.$$
$$S(\text{sphere}) = S(\text{cylinder})$$
$$= 4\pi r^2.$$

Figure   1.2

Among other results obtained by the Method of Exhaustions were the proof that the volume of a sphere is $\frac{2}{3}$ that of the circular cylinder which circumscribes it and that the area of a spherical surface is four times that of a great circle and equal to that of the curved surface of the circumscribing cylinder. (See Figure 1.2.) So important did Archimedes esteem these discoveries that he requested that a figure of a cylinder containing an inscribed sphere should be engraved on his tomb.

1.2 Intuitive Notions of Limits

We first illustrate the use of the word *limit* and some related words as they occur in everyday situations and in physical science. The statements in these illustrations are to be regarded as descriptive and not as definitions, which will be given in succeeding chapters.

If a ball is dropped from a height, it may, in its motion, be said to get closer and closer to the ground. Its distance from the ground *approaches zero*. This will be true even if the ball lands in a tree or in a basket some distance above the ground. It is clear that here is a distinction between two ways in which the distance of the ball from the ground "approaches zero." If the ball reaches the ground, its distance from the gound becomes smaller than 1 inch, smaller than 0.01 inch and, indeed, smaller than any positive distance we like to name. The distance of the ball from the ground can then be said to approach zero *as its limit*. If, on the other hand, the ball lands in a tree, its distance from the ground will remain greater than many distances that could be named. The phrase "as its limit" does not apply in this situation.

If a pail of water is raised from a well by means of a windlass and if the distance from the water level to the windlass is 20 feet, then the distance through which the pail rises approaches 20 feet. Indeed it could also be said to approach 30 feet or any distance greater than 20 feet. As in the problem of the ball, a distinction must be made here. If the pail reaches the windlass, it would be proper to say that the distance approaches 20 feet *as its limit*; this means that the difference between 20 and the number of feet through which the pail rises becomes smaller than any positive number we may name. The distance the pail rises does not get arbitrarily close to 30 feet and hence does not approach 30 feet *as its limit*. Again, if the windlass is locked so that the pail remains suspended in the well, the distance in question does not approach 20 feet *as its limit*.

A tank of water can be emptied by a tap at the bottom. The number of gallons in the tank will then approach zero even if the tap is closed before the tank is empty. But, if all the water is allowed to drain out, the number of gallons in the tank comes to differ from zero by less than any positive number and can then be said to approach zero *as its limit*.

These examples underline the association of ideas between the noun **limit** and the verb **approach**. These ideas form the subject matter of Chapters III and IV. In the examples given, the role of *time* will be recognized; the changes take place in time. In the subsequent refinement of the ideas, it will be seen that this dependence on time is not a necessary feature of the subject. Other quantities, geometrical or physical in nature, come readily to mind in relation to the ideas involved in *approach* and *limit*. Among these we include area, volume, temperature, pressure, and so on.

Sir Isaac Newton (1642–1727), one of the inventors of calculus, was not only a powerful mathematician but also a scientist with a vivid and trained imagination. His language reflects the origin of his ideas. The verb *flow* was prominent in his descriptions and the derived nouns *fluent* and *fluxion* were among his technical mathematical terms. These are not the terms in use today; they have been superseded by others that, though less suggestive, are more in line with modern interpretations of the concepts.

1.3 A Glance Backward

The centuries from the time of Archimedes to that of Newton were among the least prolific in the history of mathematics. While advances were made in arithmetic, algebra, geometry, astronomy, and dynamics, it remained for a new idea to open the flood-gates to a tidal wave of new mathematics. The break-through that gave rise to this flood was the introduction of Calculus by Newton and *Leibnitz* (1646–1716) in the seventeenth century. It was at first only "through a glass darkly" that the underlying idea of limits was seen. It took a century and a half more for this concept to emerge crystal clear as the foundation that supports much of the structure of modern mathematics. In the hands of the French mathematician *A. L. Cauchy* (1789–1857), the doctrine of limits was given its modern form.

Based on the concept of limits are three main tools of mathematical analysis. These are (i) the infinite series, (ii) the derivative, (iii) the definite integral. These do not exhaust the means employed in modern analysis, which refuses to be confined to neat categories. However, the advances resulting from the three subjects mentioned can be likened to three streams that are still increasing in volume and power.

1.4 A Bit of Advice

From the suggestions given above, the student beginning the study of limits may garner two bits of advice. (1) Give free rein to your intuition of physical situations; make use of analogies to obtain results for the truth of which you have strong physical evidence. (2) Then realize that plausibility is not proof. You must now subject yourself to the discipline of a logical chain of reasoning so that your conclusions depend, not on intuitions or feelings about physical situations but on underlying assumptions, definitions, and proved properties of numbers.

While a student of mathematics must devote time and effort to the humdrum task of mastering the bases on which the science rests, he should also derive inspiration from the vista that is foreshadowed above. The price of success is diligence but the rewards are great.

The next chapter will be given over to the spade-work necessary to provide a foundation for the exposition that follows.

Chapter II | Real Numbers, Sets, Variables, and Functions

2.1 The System of Real Numbers

Many of the properties of real numbers, given below, you have met in earlier courses; we state them here because of their application in what follows.

The simplest numbers, which were, historically, the earliest to be used, are the positive integers: 1, 2, 3, ... By successive extensions, the number system has been enlarged to include

(i) all integers, negative, zero, and positive: . . . −3, −2, −1, 0, 1, 2, 3, . . . ;

(ii) all rational numbers,* a rational number being one that can be expressed in the form p/q, where p and q are integers and $q \neq 0$;

(iii) irrational numbers, such as $\sqrt{2}$, $\sqrt{5}$, $\sqrt[3]{4}$, π, and so on.

These numbers constitute the class of all *real numbers*. (Do not try to justify the name *real*; it is an accident of the history of the number system and is to be regarded here only as a technical term.)

2.11 *The number line.* Every real number can be represented by a point on a straight line, known as the *number line* (see Figure 2.1) and, conversely, every point on the line represents a real number. The correspondence between numbers and points is so close that we shall often use the terms **integral point** and **integer** interchangeably, and likewise the terms **rational point** and **rational number**.

---

*For a complete development of the number system, we must refer to books on real-variable thory. It may be remarked, however, that, if we assume the existence and properties of the integers, it is possible to define from them the rational numbers. This development is carried out in Appendix I.

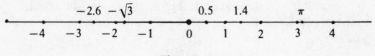

Figure 2.1

2.12 *The rational points are dense.* If r and s are two rational numbers, then any number formed from them by using the four rational operations (addition, subtraction, multiplication, and division) any number of times is also a rational number. Thus their average,

$$\frac{r + s}{2},$$

is a rational number lying in value half way between them. Hence, between any two rational numbers lies a third. Successive applications of this principle lead to the conclusion that between any two rational numbers lie an infinite number of others. This is a striking fact. Between $\frac{1}{100}$ and $\frac{1}{1000}$ are millions of rational numbers. The rational points are said to be *dense* everywhere on the number line.

2.13 *The rational numbers are countable.* The operation of counting is associated directly with the integers $1, 2, 3, \ldots$. Indeed, counting consists of setting up a one-to-one correspondence of the objects counted with the integers, beginning with 1. If the number of objects is finite, such as the number of persons in a room, of cities in a country, or of visible stars in a constellation, then the largest integer needed in the correspondence is the number of objects counted. This number can be extremely large. Think, for example, of the population of Asia or of the grains of sand on an ocean beach.

The situation is different and more interesting when the number of objects being counted is infinite, that is when the operation of selecting successive objects never ends. Suppose, for example, you are counting the numbers $1, \frac{1}{2}, \frac{1}{3}, \frac{1}{4}, \ldots$. Can an infinite set be counted? A first answer to the question is: not in the sense that one could ever finish the job if he had to repeat the corresponding integers. In a more important sense, however, some infinite sets are countable and some are not. Let us clarify this statement.

If the unit fractions given above are set down above the positive integers,

$$1, \frac{1}{2}, \frac{1}{3}, \frac{1}{4}, \frac{1}{5}, \cdots$$

$$1, 2, 3, 4, 5, \ldots$$

it is clear that the vertical alignment establishes a one-to-one correspondence so that no fraction in the list will remain uncounted. In this sense the unit fractions are *countable* or *denumerable*. Some other sets that are similarly countable are the even integers, the squares (or the cubes) of the integers, the prime integers, and the integral points (x,y) in a Cartesian plane.

Consider the rational numbers in the unit interval $0 < x < 1$. Are these numbers countable? If we attempt to count them by beginning with 0 and proceeding in order of magnitude of the numbers, we shall fail, since no rational point on the number line has another one next to it. Let us then discard the order of magnitude and attempt to count them in some other order. The problem is one of arranging the rational numbers between 0 and 1 in such an order that each one has a definite successor and every one is included just once.

$$1, \frac{1}{2}, \frac{1}{3}, \frac{2}{3}, \frac{1}{4}, \frac{3}{4}, \frac{1}{5}, \frac{2}{5}, \frac{3}{5}, \frac{4}{5}, \frac{1}{6}, \frac{5}{6}, \frac{1}{7}, \frac{2}{7}, \frac{3}{7}, \frac{4}{7}, \frac{5}{7}, \frac{6}{7}, \cdots$$

The arrangement shown here, if continued indefinitely, includes the number 1 and every rational number between 0 and 1. For example, $\frac{382}{5641}$, which is in its lowest terms, will occur a long way out in the sequence. It follows that *the rational numbers from 0 to 1 are countable.*

Exercises

1. State the principle involved in the arrangement given above.
2. Using the fact that the rational numbers from 0 to 1 are countable, show that those from 0 to 2 are countable. (Note that, if all the rational numbers from 0 to 1 are doubled, there result all the rational numbers from 0 to 2.)

3. Imagine an infinite checkerboard with two adjacent edges. Devise a method of counting all the squares of the checkerboard.

4. Suppose that, on the first row of the checkerboard of Exercise 3, the rational numbers from 0 to 1 are arranged in a counting order, on the second row those from 1 to 2, etc. Use the result of Exercise 3 to show that all positive rational numbers are countable.

5. Show that all rational numbers are countable.

6. Devise a method of counting the integral points (x, y) in a Cartesian plane.

2.14 *Are the real numbers countable?* Since, on the number line, the rational points are everywhere dense, it might be concluded that the irrational points are less numerous. This conclusion is erroneous. We must remind ourselves that a point has only position and takes up no length on the line. If the irrational points were countable, then the real points would be also. For, suppose that the irrational points as well as the rational points can be arranged in a counting order, thus:

$$r_1, r_2, r_3, \ldots \text{ for the rational points;}$$

$$i_1, i_2, i_3, \ldots \text{ for the irrational points.}$$

Then all real points can be counted in the order

$$r_1, i_1, r_2, i_2, r_3, i_3, \ldots.$$

It follows that, if we can prove that the real points are not countable, then the irrational points are not countable.

Consider all the real numbers in the unit interval from 0 to 1. These numbers can be represented in decimal form. For the rational numbers, the decimals repeat or terminate. A terminating decimal can be represented in repeating form in two ways; thus 0.24 is the same number as

$$0.24000 \ldots$$

or as

$$0.23999 \ldots.$$

In order that the decimal representations shall be unique, we shall agree to use the first of these two styles. With this understanding, every decimal of the form

$$0.a_1a_2a_3 \ldots,$$

where each of the a's is one of the 10 digits 0, 1, 2, . . . , 9, represents one and only one real number in the interval from 0 to 1.

THEOREM. *The real numbers on the unit interval are not countable.*
Proof. We shall use the indirect method of proof. Suppose, if possible, that the decimals representing these numbers can be set in a one-to-one correspondence with the integers 1, 2, 3, ... We shall write the integers in a column, each followed by its corresponding decimal.

$$1 : 0.a_{11}a_{12}a_{13} \ldots$$

$$2 : 0.a_{21}a_{22}a_{23} \ldots$$

$$3 : 0.a_{31}a_{32}a_{33} \ldots$$

$$4 : 0.a_{41}a_{42}a_{43} \ldots$$

. . . .

Our assumption is that this list includes all the numbers from 0 to 1. Now, for the contradiction, it suffices to exhibit one number that is in the interval but not in the list. Take the number

$$0.a'_{11}a'_{22}a'_{33}a'_{44} \ldots,$$

where a'_{11} is any one of the 9 digits that are different from a_{11}, a'_{22} is different from a_{22}, and so on. Hence our new number differs in at least one digit from any number in the list. Moreover we can choose the digits in the new number so that the decimal is not repeating and therefore cannot be a second representation (with 9 repeating) of a rational number already in the list. This completes the proof that there is *one* number missing from the list, no matter how the numbers in the list are chosen. Indeed there is not *only one* missing; the freedom of choice of the digits in the new-born number shows that there is a real population explosion of such numbers.

The irrational points on any interval are too numerous to be countable. Instead of the rational points "holding the line" while the irrationals penetrate it at a few points, the situation is

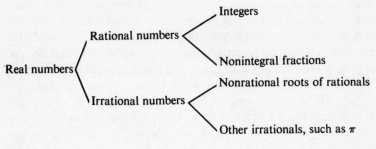

Figure   2.2

quite the reverse. The irrationals "hold the line" while the rationals, dense as they are, can be made to "stand and be counted".

The class of all real numbers, or all points on the number line, is spoken of as a *continuum*.

We append a "tree" for the real numbers. See Figure 2.2.

Exercises

1. Using the number tree, classify the following numbers: -11, $7/15$, 24, $22/7$, π, $\sqrt{49}$, -18.357, $\dfrac{1/2 + 2/3}{5/6 - 3/4}$, $\left(1 + \dfrac{1}{2} + \dfrac{1}{4} + \cdots + \dfrac{1}{64}\right)$, $\dfrac{\sqrt{5} - 1}{\sqrt{5} + 1}$, $\sqrt[3]{125}$, $6^{5/2}$, $8^{-1/3}$, π^{-1}.

2. Show that the positive square roots of non-square positive integers form a countable class of irrational numbers.
3. Show that the squares of the real numbers are not countable.

2.2 Sets

The word *set* is one of the basic words of our speech, so basic, indeed, that no mathematical definition of it will be given. *Class* and *aggregate* are sometimes used as mathematical synonyms for set. It may help to focus our ideas to describe a set of objects as any collection of objects, without regard to their order in the collection. A set of tools, a class of pupils, a flock of sheep, a herd of cattle are familiar examples of sets. The objects making up a set need not be physical objects like dishes, people, or machines; they may, instead, be immaterial objects of our thought. The commonest sets with which we shall deal are sets of numbers. We could also consider sets of lines, circles, polygons, equations, and so on. Again, a set can consist of a miscellaneous collection, such as all the objects on a teacher's desk or all those in a boy's pocket.

Sets will often be denoted by capital letters, A, B, and so on. If a stands for an object and a set A is under consideration, a pertinent question is whether or not a belongs to A. If it does, this is indicated by $a \in A$, which is read "a belongs to A" or "a is a *member* or an *element* of A". Likewise the symbolism $a \notin A$ means that a is not an element of A. The symbol ϵ (the Greek letter *epsilon*) may be called the *symbol of inclusion*.

2.3 Symbolism for a Set

The representation of a set by a single letter, although concise, gives no indication of the elements that make up the set. A symbol that gives more information is illustrated by

$$\{1, 3, 5, 7, 9\},$$

denoting the set whose elements are the first five odd integers. The same set can also be represented by

$$\{5, 7, 3, 1, 9\};$$

any other arrangement of the five digits can be used. Similarly,

$$\{1, 2, 3, \ldots n\}$$

denotes a set consisting of the first n natural numbers.

Instead of listing in brackets the elements of a set, we may describe them. This description is often abbreviated in the manner illustrated by the notation

$$\{x : x^2 - 4 = 0\},$$

which is read: the set of all values of x such that $x^2 - 4 = 0$; this set is, of course, identical with $\{2, -2\}$. Notice the translation of the colon by the words "*such that*". A vertical line is often used in

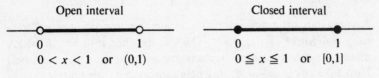

Figure 2.3

place of the colon in this notation. Finally, it may be noted that a set can be of such a bizarre nature that the description of it is best left in words. Consider, for example, the set of all positive integers less than 1000 that contain only odd digits.

2.4 Some Common Sets of Numbers

A set that is made up of n elements, where n is a nonnegative integer, is called a finite set. A finite set can have many or few elements. Indeed it is convenient to extend the meaning of *set* to include one with no elements at all. This *empty* or *null* set, usually denoted by $\emptyset$, gives an advantage to the theory of sets of much the same character as that conferred on the system of numbers by the integer 0. An infinite set is one for which the operation of counting its elements never ends. Some common infinite sets are sometimes symbolized by the following letters:

N : the set of positive integers $\{1, 2, 3, \ldots\}$;
N_0 : the set of non-negative integers $\{0, 1, 2, 3, \ldots\}$;
I : the set of all integers $\{\ldots -3, -2, -1, 0, 1, 2, 3, \ldots\}$;
Q : the set of rational numbers $\{p/q : p, q \in I, q \neq 0\}$;
R : the set of real numbers.

Some other sets can be described most conveniently in terms of the number line. Thus the set $\{x : 0 < x < 1\}$ is described as the interval from 0 to 1, excluding its end points. (See Figure 2.3) This interval and its corresponding set are usually denoted simply by $0 < x < 1$. This is called an *open* interval, in distinction from $0 \leq x \leq 1$ which includes its end points and is called *closed*.

A distinction of some importance for our present purpose is that between such sets as

$$A : \{x : 0 < x < 1\} \text{ and } B : \left\{1, \frac{1}{2}, \frac{1}{3}, \frac{1}{4}, \cdots, \frac{1}{n}, \cdots \right\}.$$

A small but arbitrary interval surrounding any point is called a *neighborhood* of the point. (This is another instance in which mathematics has appropriated a common word for a technical use.) Now take any point of *A*. *Any* neighborhood of this point contains another point of the set. (It contains an infinite number of other points; our statement expresses a minimal condition. See Exercise 8, page 16) The situation is different with the set *B*. Take, for example, the point $\frac{1}{3}$ of *B*. A sufficiently large neighborhood of this point will contain another point of the set but the neighborhood (Figure 2.4) that extends from

$$\frac{1}{2}\left(\frac{1}{2} + \frac{1}{3}\right) \quad \text{to} \quad \frac{1}{2}\left(\frac{1}{3} + \frac{1}{4}\right)$$

does not contain another point of the set *B*. Around any point of *B* a neighborhood can be specified so small that it contains no other point of *B*. Such a neighborhood of the point $1/k$ is the interval from

$$\frac{1}{2}\left(\frac{1}{k - 1} + \frac{1}{k}\right) \quad \text{to} \quad \frac{1}{2}\left(\frac{1}{k} + \frac{1}{k + 1}\right).$$

2.5 Variables

The idea behind the word *variable* has given rise to difficulties from ancient times; the philosopher Zeno confused the Athenians with the argument that an arrow shot into the air is at no time in motion since at any instant it occupies a fixed position. The definition now accepted for the word is more easily comprehended than some earlier ideas. It rests upon the concept of a set. Consider a set of four numbers $\{2, 4, 6, 8\}$, which we can write in the alternative

Figure   2.4

form

$$\{x : x = 2, 4, 6, 8\}.$$

The letter x, here used, is a symbol (some persons like the word *place-holder*) which can be replaced by any one of the four numbers of the set. This symbol is called a *variable*. The *domain* of this variable is the set $\{2, 4, 6, 8\}$. Each of the four numbers may be called a *value* or a *replacement* of the variable. Any other letter than x, or some other symbol, can be used for the variable.

Generalizing from the foregoing example, we can have for the domain of a variable any set of numbers, finite or infinite, with the exception of the empty set. If the domain has only one element, as in $\{x : x = 5\}$ then the variable is called a *constant*. We shall, of course, refer familiarly to this as the constant 5, and similarly to the constants $-\frac{1}{2}$, $\sqrt{3}$, π, and so on.

The variables of most interest in mathematical analysis are those whose domains are infinite sets. Examples of such sets are:

(1) the set of all real numbers;
(2) the set of all nonnegative real numbers;
(3) the open interval $0 < x < k$;
(4) closed intervals $a \leq x \leq b$, $-a \leq x \leq a$;
(5) the set $\{0, \frac{1}{2}, \frac{3}{4}, \frac{7}{8}, \ldots, (2^n - 1)/2^n, \ldots\}$.

Bernard Bolzano (1781-1848) was a mathematical logician who contributed to the clarification of the word *variable*. The following excerpt from a commentator on Bolzano is interesting for its mathematical content as well as for its hundred-year-old language: "Bolzano is quite clear that in mathematics and in logistics, variability is not changeableness but anyness in a specified set." (*Paradoxes of the Infinite*, translated from the German by Fr. Prihonsky, London, 1950, Routledge and K. Paul, page 35.)

Exercises

1. Express the following sets by listing their elements:
   (*i*) $\{x : x^3 - 3x^2 + 2x = 0\}$; (*ii*) $\{t : t^3 = t^2\}$;
   (*iii*) $\{y : y^{-1} \epsilon N, y \leq 10\}$.
2. List the elements of the domain of the variable x for the following sets:
   (*i*) $\{x : x \epsilon I, |x| < 6\}$;

(ii) $\{x : (x^2 - x)^2 - 8(x^2 - x) + 12 = 0\}$;
(iii) $\{x : \sqrt{x} \in N, 3 < x < 50\}$.

3. A *subset* of a set A is any set that contains all, some, or none of the elements of A. List all the possible subsets of $\{$Jack, Ted, Don, Bert$\}$.

4. Find the total number of subsets of $\{1, 2, 3, 4, 5, 6\}$.

5. Write a notation for the interval from 2 to 7, including 2 but not 7.

6. Indicate on the number line the graph of the variable x defined by $\{x : x = 1/n, n \in N, n \leqq 8\}$.

7. Indicate on the number line the graph of the variable x defined by $\{x : 2n < x < 2n + 1, n \in N_0\}$.

8. Show that, if every neighborhood of a point a on the number line contains a point, different from a, that belongs to a set A, then any such neighborhood contains an infinite number of points of A.

2.6 Functions: Some Preliminary Examples

Example 1.   Consider a graph (Figure 2.5) consisting of the four points $(1,3)$, $(2,2)$, $(3,2)$, $(4,1)$. Corresponding to each of the four values of x there is just one value of y. The set of values of x is $\{1, 2, 3, 4\}$ and the set of values of y is $\{1, 2, 3\}$. The correspondence

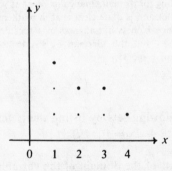

Figure   2.5

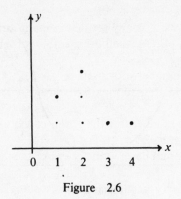

Figure 2.6

between the values of x and those of y can be indicated by

$$
\begin{array}{cc}
x & y \\
1 \longrightarrow 3 \\
2 \longrightarrow 2 \\
3 \longrightarrow 2 \\
4 \longrightarrow 1
\end{array}
$$

Example 2. Take a second graph consisting of the four points $(1,2)$, $(2,3)$, $(3,1)$, $(4,1)$. This graph (Figure 2.6) is different from that of Example 1 although the two sets of values of x are the same and likewise the two sets of values of y. The difference arises in the *correspondence* between values of x and values of y; the rule that states this correspondence in Example 1 differs from that in Example 2. In Example 2 the rule is

$$
\begin{array}{cc}
x & y \\
1 \longrightarrow 2 \\
2 \longrightarrow 3 \\
3 \longrightarrow 1 \\
4 \longrightarrow 1
\end{array}
$$

We now generalize the two foregoing examples. Consider two variables x and y, of which x takes the values in a set A and y the

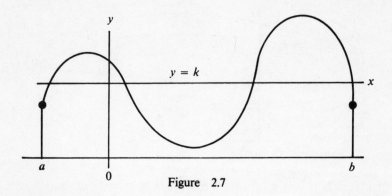

Figure   2.7

values in a set B. Suppose that, for each value of x in A, we select, by some rule, one and only one value of y in B and that the selection of the values of y exhausts the set B. We have then a correspondence in which one x corresponds to one and only one y but one y can correspond to more than one x.* An example of this is furnished by the curve sketched in Figure 2.7. The fact that, for each x, there is one and only one y means that a line parallel to the axis of y cuts the curve in just one point. On the other hand, the line $y = k$, in Figure 2.7, cuts the curve in four points; to the value $y = k$ there correspond four values of x. A point on the curve is represented by (x,y) and this notation symbolizes the correspondence between x, which stands first in the parenthesis, and y, which stands second. The interpretation of the symbol (x,y), which in geometry stands for a point, can be widened to apply to any two objects that have a definite order, indicated by the words *left* and *right*, or *first* and *second*. Such a pair of objects can be referred to as an **ordered pair**. Thus a pair of boots can be thought of as an ordered pair, meaning, not that they were ordered from a mail order catalogue, but that they are placed in the order in which they are worn—left, right.

*When the meaning is clear, the expression "one value of x" will often be abbreviated to "one x".

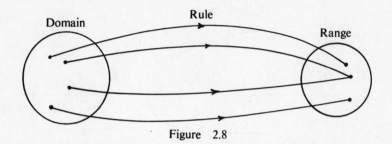

Figure 2.8

2.7 Functions: Definition

It is now clear that the correspondence between the values of x in its set and the values of y in its set implies a relation between the two sets, that is between the variables x and y. This relationship is the basis of the definition of *function*.

DEFINITION. *A set of ordered pairs (x,y) in which*
   (i) *the variable x takes on the values in a set A,*
  (ii) *each value of x corresponds to just one value of y,*
 (iii) *the corresponding values of y form a set B,*
is said to constitute a function.

The set A, of values of x, is called the **domain** of the function and the set B, of values of y, the **range** of the function. In the ordered pair (x,y) x is called the **independent variable** and y the **dependent variable**.

In the definition of function, a key role is played by the word *correspond*. The essence of the function is the **correspondence** between the values of x and those of y. The function can be represented by a single letter; the letter most commonly used is f, although F, g, and other letters are also used. Figure 2.8 illustrates schematically the roles of the *domain*, the *rule*, and the *range*. A value of y may be called the **image** of the corresponding value of x **under f**, and this may be symbolized by

$$x \xrightarrow{f} y.$$

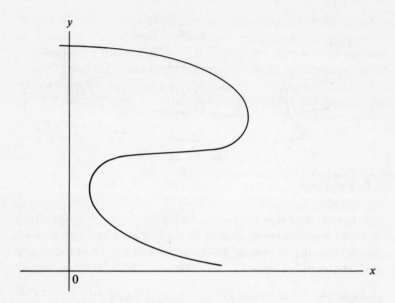

Figure 2.9

This last symbolism has obvious limitations for representing a particular function and we shall make no further use of it. The *image of x* or *value of y* is denoted by $f(x)$ and is called *the value of the function* at x.*

The definition that has been given is a very general one inasmuch as the elements of the domain and of the range can be any objects; the one thing necessary is that the correspondence provided for in the definition should exist. In what follows the elements will be restricted to real numbers.

It may be noted that, if y is a function of x, then x may or may not be a function of y. This depends on whether there is only one value of x for each value of y. In neither of the examples portrayed in Figures 2.5 and 2.6 is x a function of y, since each of these has a

---

*The definition of "values of a function" is independent of the definition of "function", inasmuch as in the former the words "set of ordered pairs" are *not* to be substituted for "function". This is just one of the double uses of a word that one has to live with.

value of y that corresponds to two values of x. The graph in Figure 2.9 does not represent a function from x to y. It should be mentioned, however, that some authors give a wider definition of function that takes in relations such as that exhibited in Figure 2.9. Such a definition makes it necessary to distinguish between *single-valued* and *many-valued* functions. All functions that satisfy the definition given above are single-valued.

2.8   Functions: Notation and Examples

It has been emphasized that the domain and range alone are not sufficient to define a function; the most important feature is the rule that establishes the correspondence. The order of ideas is: *domain, rule, range*. Of all the ways by which a correspondence between x and y can be set up, the following are the most common:

(i) by an equation connecting y with x; this equation may give the value of y in terms of x *explicitly*, as in

$$y = 2x + 5$$

or *implicitly*, as in

$$3xy + 4x + y = 5;$$

(ii) by a table of values listing corresponding pairs of numbers. In a logarithmic table, for example, a limited set of pairs $\{(x, \log x)\}$ is listed and other pairs are obtained from the table by interpolation;

(iii) by means of a graph on which points are identified with ordered pairs of numbers.

The set of ordered pairs $\{x, f(x)\}$ or $\{(x,y): y = f(x)\}$ represents the function f. The letter f, of course, has no power to select a particular function; it is used when general properties of functions or of classes of functions are under examination. We notice now some particular functions.

For the function

$$\{(x,y) : y = x^2\}$$

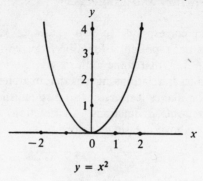

Figure   2.10

or, more briefly, $\{(x,x^2)\}$ the most useful choice for the domain is the set of real numbers; the range is then the set of non-negative real numbers. A segment of the graph of this function is sketched in Figure 2.10.

For the function

$$\{(x,y) : y = \sin x\}$$

or $\{(x, \sin x)\}$ the letter f is replaced by sin and the function is named *sine*. Its domain is taken to be the set of real numbers and its range is the interval $\{-1 \leqq x \leqq 1\}$. A portion of its graph is sketched in Figure 2.11.

A function of some importance is

$$\{(x,y) : y = |x|\}$$

or $\{(x, |x|)\}$. The symbol $|x|$ means the *absolute value* of x.

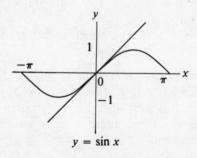

$y = \sin x$

Figure   2.11

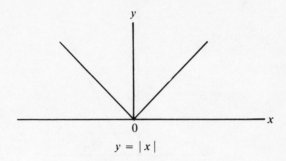

$$y = |x|$$

Figure 2.12

Thus

$$|x| = \begin{cases} x, \text{ when } x \geqq 0, \\ -x, \text{ when } x < 0. \end{cases}$$

The graph is sketched in Figure 2.12. You should become accustomed to working with absolute values. As examples,

$$|8 - 6| = |6 - 8| = 2, \quad |-5 - 2| = 7, \quad |-5 - (-2)| = 3.$$

Also $|a - b|$ is the measure of the positive distance between the points a and b on the number line.

In the study of functions we shall seldom use the circumlocutions and the symbolism that are involved in the set-builder notation. Thus the three functions last considered will be referred to as the functions x^2, $\sin x$, and $|x|$. In the same way, we shall refer to the *functions* $2x^2 - 5x + 6$, $(x + 1)/(3x - 2)$, and so on. This use of the word *function* is deeply imbedded in mathematical convention and, with the explanation that has been made, there is no point in insisting on the longer nomenclature.

2.81 *Polynomials and Rational Functions.* In elementary mathematics, functions like

$$4x - 2, \quad 3x^2, \quad x^2 + 3x + 2, \quad 2x^3 - 9x$$

are of much use. For such functions, unless it is otherwise specified, the domain will be understood to be the set of real numbers. The general function of this type has the form

$$a_0 x^n + a_1 x^{n-1} + a_2 x^{n-2} + \ldots + a_{n-1} x + a_n,$$

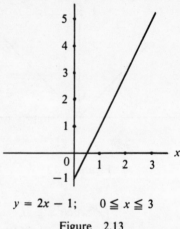

$$y = 2x - 1; \qquad 0 \leq x \leq 3$$

Figure   2.13

where n is a non-negative integer and the a's are constants. This function is called a ***polynomial***. If $a_0 \neq 0$, the integer n is called the degree of the polynomial. If $n = 0$, the polynomial reduces to a constant. If this constant is not zero, it is a polynomial of degree 0; the constant 0 fails to have a degree by the foregoing definition and we shall assign no degree to it. It follows, for example, that $x^4 - 16$ is a polynomial of degree 4 and that $\frac{3}{2}$ is a polynomial of degree 0. On the other hand, $1/x$, 2^x, and $\sin x$ are not polynomials.

Another important class of functions is exemplified by

$$\frac{3}{x}, \frac{x+1}{x-1}, x + \cfrac{1}{2x + \cfrac{1}{3x+4}}, \frac{x^3 - x}{x^2 + 1},$$

which have the form $P(x)/Q(x)$, or can be reduced to this form, where P and Q are polynomials. These functions are related to polynomials in much the same way as fractions are related to integers; they are called ***rational functions***. To complete the analogy, a rational function in which $Q(x)$ is a nonzero constant and which is therefore a polynomial, is sometimes called an *integral rational function*.

2.82   *Example 1.* The function defined by

$$y = 2x - 1,$$

with the domain $\{x : 0 \leq x \leq 3\}$ and the range $\{y : -1 \leq y \leq 5\}$ is represented by the graph in Figure 2.13. It can be described briefly as the function $2x - 1$ on the closed interval from 0 to 3. The least value of the function is -1 and the greatest value is 5.

Example 2. Consider the function defined by

$$y = 4 - x^2,$$

with the domain $\{x : -2 \leq x \leq 2\}$ and range $\{y : 0 \leq y \leq 4\}$. The graph of this function is the segment of a parabola sketched in Figure 2.14.

Example 3. The equation

$$x^2 + y^2 = 9$$

does not define a unique function. However, functions can be specified that satisfy the equation. The functions given by

$$y = \sqrt{9 - x^2} \qquad \text{and} \qquad y = -\sqrt{9 - x^2}$$

are a pair of such functions (Figure 2.15).

Exercises

1. Give the range of each of the functions defined as follows:
   (a) $y = x^2$, for $-2 < x < 2$; (b) $y = x^3$, for $-1 \leq x \leq 3$;
   (c) $y = 4/(x + 1)$, for $0 < x < \frac{1}{2}$; (d) $y = |x|$, for $-4 \leq x \leq 4$;
   (e) $y = \cos x$, for $0 \leq x \leq \pi$.

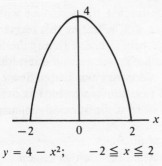

$y = 4 - x^2; \qquad -2 \leq x \leq 2$

Figure 2.14

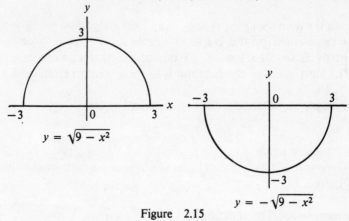

Figure 2.15

2. Draw the graphs of the functions (b) and (c) of Exercise 1.

3. Indicate by a graph joining the points (0,0) and (8,8) a set of ordered pairs (points) (x,y) such that (a) the pairs (x,y) belong to a function and the pairs (y,x) belong to a function, (b) the pairs (x,y) do not belong to a function but the pairs (y,x) do.

4. The expression $[x]$ represents *the greatest integer that is not greater than x.* Thus,

$$[\tfrac{1}{2}] = 0, \ [1] = 1, \ [2.6] = 2, \ [-3.1] = -4, \ [-5.9] = -6.$$

Construct a graph for the function $\{(x, [x])\}$ on the domain $0 \leq x \leq 6$.

5. Draw the graph of the function $\{(x,y)\}$ on the domain $-10 \leq x \leq 10$, where $y = 1$ when x is an integer and $y = 0$ when x is not an integer.

6. A graph is constructed by beginning with the line segment $y = x$ for $0 \leq x \leq 1$, reflecting this segment in the line $x = 1$ (regarded as a mirror), then reflecting the two segments in the line $x = 2$, and finally reflecting the resulting four segments in the line $x = 4$. Construct this graph. Show that in the domain $1 \leq x \leq 2$ the function represented is defined by $y = 2 - x$ or $\{(x, 2 - x)\}$. Define the function similarly for the succeeding unit intervals.

7. Draw a graph of the function defined by each of the following expressions. Indicate for each its largest possible domain and

the corresponding range. (a) $|x - 1|$, (b) $-|x^3|$, (c) $\sqrt{1 - (x - 2)^2}$, (d) $\cos x$.

8. Describe the location of the points (x,y) on the domain $0 \leq x \leq 1$ for which $y = 1$ when x is a rational number and $y = 0$ when x is an irrational number. Is it possible to draw the graph of the function so defined?

9. Describe the location of the points on the domain $0 \leq x \leq 1$ for which $y = x$ when x is a rational number and $y = -x$ when x is an irrational number.

10. In the x,y plane a circle is drawn with center $(a,0)$ and radius r units. Is this circle the graph of a function of x? Is it the graph of two functions of x? If so, specify two such functions.

11. The function $y = \sin ax$, defined for all real values of x, ax being the radian measure of an angle, is *periodic* with *period* $2\pi/a$. This means that $\sin ax$ has the same value as $\sin a(x + 2\pi/a)$ for all values of x. Using the sine, construct a function with period $\frac{2}{3}$; using the cosine, construct a function with period $3\pi/4$.

12. Recall that division by 0 is not a defined operation in mathematics and therefore fractions with vanishing denominators are strictly to be excluded as meaningless. What values of x must be excluded in the domain of $\tan x$? What values for $\cot x$, for $\sec x$, and for $\csc x$?

13. From the following list, select the rational functions and from these select the polynomials:

(a) $x + 1/x$, (b) $(x - 1)(x - 2)(x - 3)$, (c) $x + \sqrt{x} + 1$, (d) $3/x + 4/x^2$, (e) $2^x - 2$, (f) $x^{10} + 4x^5 + 5$, (g) $\log (x^2 + 1)$.

Chapter III | Limits of Sequences

3.1 Sequences

In our discussion of sets, it was pointed out that a set is independent of the order of the objects that compose it. The question of the order of the elements in a set is not raised, any more than that of the tubers in a sack of potatoes. When the property of *order* is imposed on the elements of a set, the result is a *sequence*. The positive integers in their natural order

$$1, 2, 3, 4, \ldots$$

form a sequence. Other examples are:

$1^2, 2^2, 3^2, 4^2, \ldots,$ the squares of the positive integers;
$1, 3, 5, 7, \ldots,$ the odd positive integers;
$1, 2, 3, 5, 7, \ldots,$ the prime integers;
$1, 1, 2, 3, 5, 8, \ldots,$ the Fibonacci numbers, each term, after the second, being the sum of the two preceding terms;

$$\frac{1}{2}, \frac{2}{3}, \frac{3}{4}, \frac{4}{5}, \cdots, \frac{n}{n+1}, \cdots$$

The *terms* of a sequence are usually, though not always, separated by commas. In distinction from a set, it is immaterial whether or not the sequence is enclosed in brackets.

DEFINITION. *A set of numbers arranged in order, so that there is a first one and every number is followed by another, its successor, is called an* **infinite sequence**.

The force of the word *infinite* in this definition is that the sequence in question has no last term. The terms continue on and on in unbroken sequence.

In the decimal form of

$$\frac{5}{11} = 0.454545\ldots,$$

the digits in the decimal constitute a sequence which, since the decimal is recurring, is easily continued as far as we wish. Similarly, the digits of the number

$$\pi = 3.1415926\ldots$$

form a sequence; each digit has a definite successor, which requires some labor to compute and of which more than 100,000 have been found with the aid of an electronic computer.

To interchange two terms in a sequence does not change the *set* of numbers but gives a different *sequence*. Although we shall confine our attention to numbers, the elements of a sequence need not be so confined. Thus, one could consider sequences of *points*, *lines*, *circles*, *angles*, *functions*, and so on.

A set that has a first term and a last term and in which each term except the last has a successor is a *finite sequence*. We shall not be concerned with finite sequences. When the word sequence alone is used, it will be understood to refer to an infinite sequence.

Since a 1–1 correspondence exists between the terms of any sequence and the natural numbers, it follows that the terms of any sequence form a countable set. The symbol

$$a_1, a_2, a_3, \ldots, a_n, \ldots,$$

which can stand for any sequence, will be denoted, for brevity, by

$$(a_n).$$

Another aspect of the 1–1 correspondence is that *the set of ordered pairs* $\{(n, a_n)\}$, *where n takes the values* 1, 2, 3, . . . , *constitutes a function whose domain is the set N of positive integers.* When it is useful to emphasize this fact, we write $a_n = f(n)$.

Our study of (a_n) will be concerned with the behavior* of the terms as n assumes in succession larger and larger values. In some

---

*Mathematicians use the word *behavior* in a different sense from that used by psychologists. The behavior of a sequence refers to the characteristics of the succession of terms. A single term has no "behavior problem".

sequences one gets a correct impression of this behavior from the first few terms; in others first impressions may be deceptive. The mere fact that the sequence is endless requires an effort of imagination. The first billion terms are only a beginning of the sequence; after a thousand billion terms we are no nearer to an end of the sequence than we were at the beginning.

3.2 Bounded and Unbounded Sequences

Keeping in mind that our interest in a sequence (a_n) is bound up with increasingly large values of n, we examine three simple sequences:

(i) $1, 1, 1, \ldots,$ with each term 1;
(ii) $1, -1, 1, -1, \ldots,$ with alternating signs;
(iii) $2, 4, 6, 8, \ldots,$ the even positive integers.

When only the first few terms of a sequence are given, there is always doubt regarding the following terms. In the sequence (i), it is specified that each term is 1. If this had not been specified, we could not be sure of the fourth and following terms. Suppose, for example, that the nth term of a sequence is

$$1 + (n - 1)(n - 2)(n - 3)/6.$$

The first six terms are then

$$1, 1, 1, 2, 5, 11,$$

of which the first three are those of (i). *When the nth term is expressed in terms of n, the sequence is completely determined.* It should be noted, however, that the expression for the nth term must have a value for every positive integral value of n. The "sequence"

$$\left(\frac{n + 5}{n - 5} \right)$$

has no fifth term.

The terms of (i) are all the same; this sequence has very little interest. The terms of (ii) alternate from 1 to -1 and do not settle down to any fixed number. The terms of (iii) increase beyond all bounds, becoming greater than a billion billion, for example. These three sequences provide the illustration for the following definition.

DEFINITION. *A sequence whose terms are all less than or equal to the same number, G, is said to be bounded above. The number G is called an upper bound.*

A similar definition for a lower bound is left for the reader to formulate. It is clear that, for the sequence (i), the number 1 is both an upper bound and a lower bound; for (ii), 1 is an upper bound and −1 a lower bound. The sequence (iii) has the lower bound 2 but has no upper bound. A sequence that has both an upper and a lower bound will be described as **bounded**. It is to be noted that a bound of a sequence is not a unique number; if G is an upper bound, then any number $> G$ is also an upper bound and the sequence may or may not have upper bounds less than G.

Example 1. Examine the boundedness of the sequence

$$0, \frac{3}{5}, \frac{8}{10}, \frac{15}{17}, \ldots, \frac{n^2 - 1}{n^2 + 1}, \ldots$$

Solution. Since $n^2 - 1 < n^2 + 1$, the nth term is < 1. Also no term is negative. It follows that the nth term $\geqq 0$ and < 1 for all values of n. Hence the sequence is bounded.

Example 2. Examine, for boundedness, the sequence

$$0, \frac{3}{2}, \frac{8}{3}, \frac{15}{4}, \ldots, \frac{n^2 - 1}{n}, \ldots$$

Solution. The nth term of this sequence is

$$\frac{n^2 - 1}{n} = n - \frac{1}{n}.$$

From this nth term one conjectures that the sequence is unbounded. For a proof we notice that, while the nth term is not $> n$, it is greater than $n - 1$, if $n > 1$, since

$$n - \frac{1}{n} = n - 1 + \left(1 - \frac{1}{n}\right).$$

No matter what large number G is chosen, $n - 1$ becomes $> G$. Hence the sequence is unbounded.

3.3 Two Important Types of Sequence

Of all the modes of behavior of a sequence, two, of special importance, will now be illustrated and defined.

In the sequence (n) or

$$1, 2, 3, 4, \ldots, n, \ldots,$$

the terms increase without bound. After the 1000th term, every term is greater than 1000. On the other hand, the sequence $((-1)^{n-1}n)$ or

$$1, -2, 3, -4, 5, -6, \ldots$$

is unbounded both above and below but it differs from (n) in that there is no term after which the terms are *all* greater than 1000. Similarly, given any large number G, *there is no integer m such that the nth term is greater than G for all values of $n > m$*. Take next for (a_n) the sequence

$$2, 4, 6, 8, \ldots, 2n, \ldots,$$

in which $a_n = 2n$. If we require a_n to be greater than 10^8, say, this requirement is met by taking

$$n > \frac{1}{2}(10)^8;$$

to make $a_n > G$ it is sufficient to take $n > m$, where $m = \frac{1}{2}G$.

DEFINITION. *If, when any number G is chosen,* as large as we please, it is possible to match it with an integer m such that, for all values of n greater than or equal to m, a_n is greater than or equal to G, then the sequence (a_n) is said to become infinite or to tend to infinity.*

We use the symbolism

$$a_n \to \infty \qquad \text{as} \qquad n \to \infty.$$

While this symbolism is sanctioned by usage, it has its pitfalls: *there is no number ∞; the arrows do not imply that either n or a_n becomes close to any number.* You should beware of reading more into the symbols than is stated in the definition.

---

*Think, if you like, of G as the initial letter of "Great Big Number."

In order to illustrate the second and more significant mode of behavior of a sequence, consider again the sequence

$$0, \frac{3}{5}, \frac{8}{10}, \frac{15}{17}, \cdots, \frac{n^2 - 1}{n^2 + 1}, \cdots$$

The 10th term of this sequence is $\frac{99}{101}$ and the 100th term is $\frac{9999}{10001}$. It seems plausible that the nth term becomes closer and closer to 1 as n increases. How close to 1 does the nth term become? A first answer might be *"as close as we please"*. It will be a measure of a student's growth in understanding of mathematics if he realizes the inadequacy of this language as a basis from which to deduce conclusions. Our problem is to replace this vague idea by an exact statement.

Does the difference of the nth term from 1 become less than $\frac{1}{1000}$, for example? This will be true if

$$1 - \frac{n^2 - 1}{n^2 + 1} < \frac{1}{1000},$$

that is, if

$$\frac{2}{n^2 + 1} < \frac{1}{1000},$$

or if

$$n^2 + 1 > 2000.$$

This requires that

$$n^2 > 1999,$$

which is satisfied if

$$n \geq 45.$$

It is readily seen that this method is not confined in its application to the number $\frac{1}{1000}$. Whatever small **margin** or **tolerance** we are willing to allow between 1 and $(n^2 - 1)/(n^2 + 1)$, we can find an integer, say m, such that, *for all values of $n \geq m$*, the nth term of the sequence is within the allowed margin from 1. This fact is expressed by saying that the *sequence approaches the limit* 1 *as n becomes infinite*. We now fix this concept by a definition.

DEFINITION. *A sequence (a_n) is said to approach a limit L if, given any positive number ϵ, no matter how small, there exists a positive integer m large enough so that*

$$|a_n - L| \leq \epsilon$$

for all values of $n \geq m$. Notice that the inequality $|a_n - L| \leq \epsilon$ can be written in the alternative form

$$L - \epsilon \leq a_n \leq L + \epsilon.$$

A sequence that approaches a limit is said to **converge** or to be **convergent**. A sequence that does not converge is **divergent**. We note that, whereas a sequence that tends to infinity is divergent, the converse is not necessarily true. The sequence

$$1, -1, 1, -1, \ldots$$

with alternating signs, is divergent (that is, not convergent) although no term is > 1 or < -1.

The idea that a sequence (a_n) approaches a limit L can be indicated by the symbolism

$$(a_n) \to L \quad \text{as} \quad n \to \infty$$

or, alternatively, by

$$\lim_{n \to \infty} a_n = L.$$

In the definition, the words "*approach a limit*" are given a precise meaning. It is not a definition of the word "*approach*" by itself. While it is suggestive to think of a_n creeping up to its limit by short stages, it must be emphasized that the definition is quite independent of either *time* or *motion*.

The definition will repay further study. The idea that we reduce to arithmetical terms is: *by making n large enough, we make a_n as close as we please to L.* Here n is mentioned first and a_n second but in the test for a limit this order is reversed; *we specify a tolerance for a_n first and then search for an integer n to match it.* It is instructive, and may be amusing, to recast the test in the form of a game or contest between two players. Player A announces a small number ϵ, say 10^{-4}, and challenges player B to produce an integer m such that, for every n greater than m, $|a_n - L|$ is $\leq \epsilon$. If B can win this game from A for every ϵ that A can choose, then L is the limit of the sequence.

Let us apply our method to the sequence

$$\frac{1}{2}, \frac{3}{4}, \frac{7}{8}, \frac{15}{16}, \ldots, \frac{2^n - 1}{2^n}, \ldots$$

From the form of the nth term it is a natural conjecture that this sequence approaches the limit 1 and this we shall prove. Since

$$a_n = \frac{2^n - 1}{2^n},$$

the difference of a_n from 1 is

$$1 - a_n = \frac{1}{2^n}.$$

Suppose that player A demands a margin of 10^{-4}. This requires that

$$\frac{1}{2^n} < \frac{1}{10^4}$$

or that

$$2^n > 10000.$$

This inequality is satisfied if $n \geq 14$ and hence $m = 14$ is a proper choice for player B. The same reasoning will enable B to match A's choice of any ϵ which, remember, must be positive but can be ever so small. Finally, we note again that B's choice depends on A's; *A must choose first.*

3.4 Monotone Sequences

Consider the two sequences

(i) $0, 1, 2, 3, 4, \ldots, n - 1, \ldots$
(ii) $1, 0, 3, 2, 5, 4, \ldots,$ in which the $(2n - 1)$th term is $2n - 1$ and the $2n$th term is $2n - 2$.

In (i) each term after the first is greater than the preceding term. The terms are said to increase *monotonically* with n. This property does not hold for (ii). The distinction just made is the basis of the following definition.

DEFINITION. *A sequence in which each term after the first is at least as great as its predecessor is said to be a monotone increasing sequence.* A corresponding definition applies to a monotone decreasing sequence.

Another example of a monotone increasing sequence is

$$1, \frac{3}{2}, \frac{5}{3}, \frac{7}{4}, \cdots, \frac{2n-1}{n}, \cdots$$

Besides being monotone, this sequence is bounded, since

$$\frac{2n-1}{n} = 2 - \frac{1}{n} < 2$$

for all values of n. Let the terms of this sequence be represented on the number line (Figure 3.1). In the resulting sequence of points, each, after the first, is to the right of its predecessor and to the left of 2. Since the successive points are closer and closer to 2, it seems clear that one of two conditions must apply: (i) the points approach 2 as their limit or (ii) the points approach as their limit some point to the left of 2. In fact it is easily shown by the ϵ, m method that the limit is 2. From this example you will probably be willing to accept the truth of the following theorem.

THEOREM. *A monotone increasing (decreasing) sequence that is bounded above (below) approaches a limit.*

It is one thing to accept this theorem because "you do not see how it can fail to be true", and another to give a conclusive proof. A proof is given in Appendix II at the end of this book.

3.5 *Example 1.* Test for convergence the sequence

$$0, \frac{7}{4}, \frac{26}{9}, \frac{63}{16}, \frac{124}{25}, \cdots, \frac{n^3-1}{n^2}, \cdots.$$

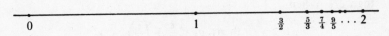

Figure 3.1

Solution. The nth term is

$$a_n = n. - \frac{1}{n^2}.$$

Now n increases without bound and it seems intuitively clear that $1/n^2$ dwindles away toward 0. This provides the clue to the fact that the sequence diverges. To prove this let player A choose a large number G. For what values of n can B be sure that

$$n - \frac{1}{n^2} > G?$$

For this to be true it is necessary that n be greater than G but this may not be sufficient. Since, however, the two sides of the inequality are nearly equal when n is replaced by G, it seems probable that the inequality will hold if n is any integer greater than or equal to $G + 1$. Now

$$G + 1 - \frac{1}{(G + 1)^2} > G, \quad \text{since} \quad 1 - \frac{1}{(G + 1)^2} > 0.$$

Hence it suffices for player B to choose for m the smallest integer that is $\geq G + 1$. Then $a_n > G$ whenever $n \geq m$. This means that $(a_n) \to \infty$ as $n \to \infty$ and the sequence is divergent.

Example 2. Test for convergence the sequence

$$2, \frac{3}{4}, \frac{4}{9}, \frac{5}{16}, \cdots, \frac{n + 1}{n^2}, \cdots$$

Solution. We have

$$a_n = \frac{1}{n} + \frac{1}{n^2}.$$

Our intuition tells us that $a_n \to 0$ as $n \to \infty$. To verify this, choose any small positive number ϵ. Take for m the integer next greater than $2/\epsilon$. When

$$n > \frac{2}{\epsilon}, \quad \text{then} \quad a_n < \frac{\epsilon}{2} + \left(\frac{\epsilon}{2}\right)^2 < \epsilon.$$

The condition for a limit is satisfied and $a_n \to 0$ as $n \to \infty$.

Example 3. Prove that, if a sequence (a_n) of non-negative terms tends to 0, then the sequence

$$\left(\frac{a_1 + a_2 + \ldots + a_n}{n}\right)$$

of the arithmetic means of the first n terms also tends to 0.

Proof. The proof of this theorem requires some care and is a good example of the ϵ, m method. Since $(a_n) \to 0$, then, given any small ϵ, we can choose an integer m such that, for $n \geqq m$, $a_n < \epsilon/2$. Now

$$\frac{a_1 + a_2 + \ldots + a_n}{n} = \frac{a_1 + a_2 + \ldots + a_m}{n} + \frac{a_{m+1} + \ldots + a_n}{n}.$$

Of the two fractions on the right, the numerator of the first is independent of n; it is therefore a constant, which we shall denote by K. In the numerator of the second fraction, each of the $n - m$ terms is positive (or zero) and less than $\epsilon/2$. Hence we have

$$\frac{a_1 + a_2 + \ldots + a_n}{n} < \frac{K}{n} + \frac{\epsilon}{2} \frac{n - m}{n}$$

$$< \frac{K}{n} + \frac{\epsilon}{2},$$

since $(n - m)/n < 1$. Now for n choose an integer m' so large that

$$\frac{K}{m'} < \frac{\epsilon}{2}.$$

It may be that the number m previously chosen will suffice; if not, we choose a larger number. With this choice, we have

$$\frac{a_1 + a_2 + \ldots + a_n}{n} < \frac{\epsilon}{2} + \frac{\epsilon}{2} = \epsilon.$$

This means that, given any small positive ϵ, we have chosen an integer m' which assures that

$$\left(\frac{a_1 + a_2 + \ldots + a_n}{n}\right) \to 0 \quad \text{as} \quad n \to \infty.$$

Exercises /A

1. Write the numerical values of the first 5 terms of each of the following sequences:

   (a) $(n^2 - 3n + 2)$,   (b) $\left(\dfrac{4n - 3}{3n + 2}\right)$,   (c) $(1 + (-1)^n)$,

   (d) $\left(\left(\dfrac{n + 1}{n}\right)^n\right)$,   (e) $(2^n/n^2)$,   (f) $\left(\sin\dfrac{n\pi}{2}\right)$.

2. State, without proofs, which of the following sequences approach limits, which tend to infinity, and which do neither:
   (a) $1, \frac{1}{3}, \frac{1}{5}, \ldots, 1/(2n - 1), \ldots$
   (b) $1, 1, \frac{1}{2}, 2, \frac{1}{3}, 3, \ldots$, in which the $2n$th term is n and the $(2n - 1)$th term is $1/n$.
   (c) $1, -\frac{1}{2}, \frac{1}{3}, -\frac{1}{4}, \ldots, (-1)^{n-1}/n, \ldots$
   (d) $1, 3, 2, 4, 5, 7, 6, 8, 9, \ldots$, in which odd and even pairs alternate.
   (e) $1, 2, 1, 1, 2, 1, 1, 1, 2, 1, 1, 1, 1, 2, \ldots$, in which each group of 1's has one more than its predecessor.

3. Which, if any, of the sequences given in Exercise 2 are monotone?

4. The sequence (a_n), where $a_n = n^2/100$, tends to ∞ as $n \to \infty$. Calculate the least integer m such that $a_n > 10^6$, for all $n > m$.

5. The sequence (a_n), where $a_n = (n^2 + 10^4)/n$, tends to ∞. Calculate the least integer m such that $a_n > 400$, for all $n > m$.

6. The sequence (a_n), where $a_n = 1/(3n^2 - 100)$, tends to 0 as $n \to \infty$. Given $\epsilon = \frac{1}{500}$, calculate the least integer m such that $a_n < \epsilon$ whenever $n \geqq m$.

7. In order to prove that $(1/(3n + 1)) \to 0$, a small number ϵ has been chosen. Calculate, in terms of ϵ, a suitable matching integer m.

8. In order to prove that $((n + 1)/(3n - 1)) \to \frac{1}{3}$ as $n \to \infty$, calculate an integer m to match the constant $\epsilon = \frac{1}{100}$.

Exercises /B

9. State the limit approached by $(3n/(5n + 2))$ and give an ϵ,m proof.

10. State the limit approached by $(n/(n^2 + 1))$ and give an ϵ,m proof.

11. Show that, if (a_n) is a monotone increasing sequence of positive numbers, then

$$\left(\frac{a_1 + a_2 + \ldots + a_n}{n} \right)$$

is also monotone increasing.

12. Prove the theorem corresponding to Exercise 11 for a monotone decreasing sequence.

13. Show that

$$\left(\frac{1 + \dfrac{1}{2} + \dfrac{1}{3} + \cdots + \dfrac{1}{n}}{n} \right)$$

is monotone decreasing.

14. Show that

$$\left(\frac{1 + 2^{-1} + 4^{-1} + \cdots + 2^{1-n}}{n} \right)$$

tends to 0 as $n \to \infty$.

15. Prove the following corollary to Example 3: If the sequence (a_n) of positive numbers $\to h$ as $n \to \infty$, then the sequence

$$\left(\frac{a_1 + a_2 + \cdots + a_n}{n} \right)$$

also $\to h$.

16. Show that

$$\left(\frac{2 + \dfrac{3}{2} + \dfrac{4}{3} + \cdots + \left(\dfrac{n + 1}{n} \right)}{n} \right) \to 1$$

as $n \to \infty$.

Chapter IV | Limits of Functions

4.1 Functions with Real Domains

If the domain of a function is the set N of positive integers, the function has been described as a sequence. We shall now be concerned with functions on less restricted domains that can be specified interchangeably as sets of numbers or sets of points. The following sets of real numbers are examples of useful and familiar domains:

 (*i*) the whole number line;
 (*ii*) the positive half of the number line;
 (*iii*) an *interval* from a to b, which may be open: $a < x < b$, or closed: $a \leqq x \leqq b$, or open at one end and closed at the other.

Just as any arbitrarily chosen set can be the domain of a function, so also the range can be chosen arbitrarily, subject only to the condition that each point of the domain shall correspond to one and only one point of the range. In this chapter, unless it is otherwise specified, the domain of a function will be understood to be the set of real numbers.

Of all the ways of setting up the correspondence, the one that has the longest history and with which you are most familiar is the use of a single expression involving the independent variable. As an example, the function $\{(x,y): y = x^2\}$ can be referred to as the function defined by $y = x^2$ and this will sometimes be abbreviated to "the function x^2". It is the second variable, y, in the set of ordered pairs $\{(x,y)\}$ that is of prime concern in the following discussion of limits.

41

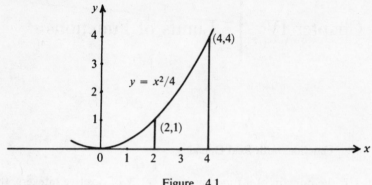

Figure 4.1

4.2 Limits: A Preliminary Discussion

The definition of limits of sequences, studied in Chapter III, will furnish the clue for the discussion of limits of more general functions.

As a first example we consider the function

$$\left\{ (x,y) : y = \frac{x^2}{4} \right\}.$$

A portion of the graph of this function is sketched in Figure 4.1. When $x = 2$, $y = 1$; the ordered pair $(2,1)$ represents a point on the graph. It appears either from the graph or from the equation $y = x^2/4$ that, when x is close to 2, y is close to 1. How close to 1 does $x^2/4$ become? A first answer is *"as close as we please"*. Then how is this closeness to be achieved? We answer *"by taking x sufficiently close to 2"*. We have here two suggestive but vague phrases: "as close as we please" and "sufficiently close"; we proceed to incorporate these ideas in a precise statement.

For this purpose we call again on our two players A and B. Suppose that A demands that $x^2/4$ should differ from 1 by a margin of $\frac{1}{2}$ or less. B's play is to search, not for a large integer as in the case of a sequence, but for a corresponding margin for the difference between x and 2. In order that $x^2/4$ should differ from 1 by not more than $\frac{1}{2}$, it is necessary and it is sufficient that

$$1 - \frac{1}{2} \leqq \frac{x^2}{4} \leqq 1 + \frac{1}{2}.$$

These inequalities reduce to

$$2 \leqq x^2 \leqq 6,$$

which are satisfied if

$$1.414 \leqq x \leqq 2.449,$$

that is, if

$$2 - 0.586 \leqq x \leqq 2 + 0.449.$$

Now player B can choose the smaller of the two numbers 0.586 and 0.449. If x is within a margin of 0.449 from 2, then $x^2/4$ will be within the proposed margin of $\frac{1}{2}$ from 1. We emphasize that the inequalities are satisfied if x differs from 2 by 0.449 or *by any positive number less than* 0.449. We write

$$|x - 2| \leqq 0.449.$$

Suppose we take a different value for $x^2/4$ and let A choose the same margin, $\frac{1}{2}$, as before. Will B's former choice of a margin now match A's choice? Let A demand that $x^2/4$ should differ from 4 by not more than $\frac{1}{2}$. It appears that x should be close to 4. To satisfy A's requirement we must have

$$4 - \frac{1}{2} \leqq \frac{x^2}{4} \leqq 4 + \frac{1}{2},$$

which reduces to

$$14 \leqq x^2 \leqq 18.$$

This is satisfied by

$$3.742 \leqq x \leqq 4.242,$$

that is, by

$$4 - 0.258 \leqq x \leqq 4 + 0.242.$$

It follows that B should choose a margin of 0.242 for the difference between x and 4.

The foregoing example makes clear that the margin chosen by B depends, not only on the margin chosen by A, but also on the value

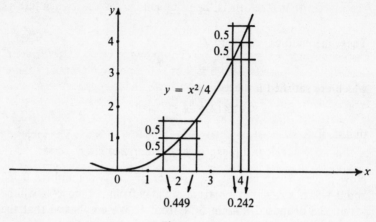

Figure   4.2

of x that is chosen in advance. Beginning with $x = 2$ and a margin
of $\frac{1}{2}$ chosen by A, we found that a suitable margin for B to choose is
0.449. Again, for $x = 4$ and the same margin of $\frac{1}{2}$, B must narrow
his margin to 0.242. This is illustrated in Figure 4.2.

Let us return to the value $x = 2$. We are not yet ready to assert
that $x^2/4$ approaches the limit 1 as x approaches 2 although this is
clearly suggested. In fact A's margin of $\frac{1}{2}$ is not the only one that
could be chosen and much smaller margins can be used. In order
not to be entangled in a maze of arithmetic, let us make use of a bit
of algebra. For the margin proposed by A we could use a letter;
the letter that has become conventional for this purpose is the
Greek letter ϵ which has already been used in the discussion of limits
of sequences. The essential requirement for the number ϵ is that it
be a real number, *greater than* 0, and that it can be as small as
player A wishes to choose. Also, having been chosen, it must
remain fixed throughout the problem in which it is being used.

If A proposes the margin of ϵ for the difference of $x^2/4$ from 1,
B must then reason as follows: we want

$$1 - \epsilon \leqq \frac{x^2}{4} \leqq 1 + \epsilon,$$

which requires that

$$2\sqrt{1 - \epsilon} \leqq x \leqq 2\sqrt{1 + \epsilon}.$$

The margin that B selects is then the smaller of the two numbers

$$2 - 2\sqrt{1 - \epsilon} \quad \text{and} \quad 2\sqrt{1 + \epsilon} - 2.$$

Using conventional symbols, we denote by the Greek letter δ (delta) the smaller of these two numbers or some positive number smaller than either. Then the statement with which we began: "*$x^2/4$ can be made as close as we please to 1 by making x sufficiently close to 2*" is now transformed into the precise statement "*$x^2/4$ differs from 1 by less than ϵ whenever x differs from 2 by less than δ*". The meaning of this statement can be expressed in the alternative form: "*$x^2/4$ approaches 1 as its limit when x approaches 2*", and in symbols by

$$\lim_{x \to 2} \frac{x^2}{4} = 1.$$

4.3   The Geometric Interpretation

In Figure 4.2 consider the point $(2,1)$. The requirement that $x^2/4$ shall differ from 1 by not more than $\frac{1}{2}$ can be visualized by drawing two horizontal lines $y = 1 - \frac{1}{2}$ and $y = 1 + \frac{1}{2}$. These lines delimit a band of width 1 unit, within which the points representing values of $x^2/4$ are required to lie. To meet this requirement we draw two vertical lines

$$x = 2 - 0.449 \quad \text{and} \quad x = 2 + 0.449.$$

These lines delimit a vertical band within which the points $(x, x^2/4)$ must lie. By their intersection the two bands form a rectangle with sides parallel to the two axes. All points on the graph of $y = x^2/4$ that lie in the vertical band must also lie in the horizontal band. This means that, if the graph does not pass through any vertex of the rectangle, it crosses the vertical sides of the rectangle and not the horizontal sides.

Consider now the point $(4,4)$ on the graph. If we take a horizontal band of width 1 unit centered on the line $y = 4$, we require the vertical band, centered on the line $x = 4$, to have a total width of 0.484 or less.

Let us now generalize the ideas used in the preceding example. Given any function, defined by $y = f(x)$ (Figure 4.3), suppose we have reason for thinking that $\lim_{x \to a} f(x) = L$. On the graph mark the

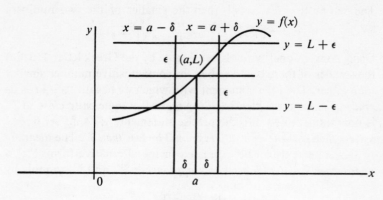

Figure   4.3

point (a, L). Corresponding to a proposed margin ϵ, for $f(x)$, we draw the two lines

$$y = L - \epsilon \qquad \text{and} \qquad y = L + \epsilon,$$

forming an ϵ band. If we are able to find a corresponding margin δ, for x, we draw the two vertical lines

$$x = a - \delta \qquad \text{and} \qquad x = a + \delta,$$

which form a δ band. The two bands intersect to form a "trap" in which all the points are "caught" that satisfy

$$y = f(x) \qquad \text{and} \qquad a - \delta \leqq x \leqq a + \delta.$$

All points that satisfy $y = f(x)$ and that are in the δ band are in the ϵ,δ rectangle; there may, however, be points in the ϵ band that satisfy $y = f(x)$ and that are not in the ϵ,δ rectangle. This is illustrated in Figure 4.3.

4.4   Definition and Remarks

DEFINITION.   *Consider a function defined by a set of ordered pairs* $\{(x, f(x))\}$ *and let a be a fixed number. The variable $f(x)$ is said to approach a limit L as x approaches a if, given any positive number ϵ, no matter how small, we can find a positive number δ, such that*

$$|f(x) - L| \leqq \epsilon$$

for all values of x, different from a, for which

$$|x - a| \leqq \delta.$$

When the limit exists, we shall use the symbolism

$$\lim_{x \to a} f(x) = L$$

[read "the limit of $f(x)$ as x approaches a equals L"] or the alternative symbolism

$$f(x) \to L \qquad \text{as} \qquad x \to a$$

[read "$f(x)$ tends to the limit L as x tends to a"].

Remarks on this definition. (i) The definition of $\lim_{x \to a} f(x)$ makes no use of $f(a)$, the value of f at a. Indeed the function f need not be defined at a. If $(a, f(a))$ belongs to the function, it may be deleted from the function or $f(a)$ may be replaced by any other number without in any way affecting the limit in question.

(ii) The values of $f(x)$ in the neighborhood of $x = a$ may be less than, equal to, or greater than the limit L. In the example: $\lim_{x \to 2} x^2/4 = 1$, the values assumed by $x^2/4$ for $x < 2$ are less than the limit and the values assumed for $x > 2$ are greater than the limit.

(iii) When the graph of the function $\{(x, f(x))\}$ is drawn, it usually suggests what the limit of $f(x)$ is as $x \to a$, if such limit exists. Even without explicit values of ϵ and δ, if the horizontal and vertical bands can be drawn to satisfy the conditions stated above, this evidence is sufficient. This will be illustrated in the examples that follow.

4.5 Examples and Further Discussion

Example 1. Investigate $\lim_{x \to 2} (1/x)$.

Solution. The graph (Figure 4.4) suggests strongly that this limit exists and equals $\frac{1}{2}$. The evidence furnished by the ϵ and δ bands

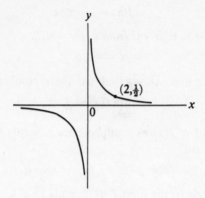

Figure   4.4

would ordinarily be sufficient. It is, however, a useful exercise to give an analytic proof.

Given a small positive number ϵ (the graph suggests that we take $\epsilon < \frac{1}{2}$) we demand that

$$\left| \left(\frac{1}{x} \right) - \frac{1}{2} \right| \leqq \epsilon$$

which means that

$$\frac{1}{2} - \epsilon \leqq \frac{1}{x} \leqq \frac{1}{2} + \epsilon.$$

This reduces to

$$\frac{2}{1 - 2\epsilon} \geqq x \geqq \frac{2}{1 + 2\epsilon}$$

and, since we are interested in the difference between x and 2, we write the last inequalities in the form

$$2 + \frac{4\epsilon}{1 - 2\epsilon} \geqq x \geqq 2 - \frac{4\epsilon}{1 + 2\epsilon}.$$

Now take

$$\delta = \frac{4\epsilon}{1 + 2\epsilon}$$

since this is the smaller of the two fractions. We require that

$$|x - 2| \leqq \delta.$$

Our conclusion is that

$$\left|\left(\frac{1}{x}\right) - \frac{1}{2}\right| \leqq \epsilon$$

for all values of x such that $|x - 2| \leqq \delta$. This proves that $\lim_{x \to 2} (1/x) = \frac{1}{2}$.

The function $1/x$ will repay further study. It is not defined when $x = 0$. As we have seen, the lack of a value for $f(x)$ at $x = 0$ does not, in itself, preclude the possibility of a limit as $x \to 0$. Does $\lim_{x \to 0} (1/x)$ exist? The graph furnishes the answer. No matter how narrow a δ band is drawn, centered on the y axis, the part of the graph within this band is not confined to any horizontal ϵ band, no matter how wide it may be. Hence $1/x$ has neither a value when $x = 0$ nor a limit as $x \to 0$.

Example 2. Consider the function $\{(x, f(x))\}$ defined by the graph of Figure 4.5. This is a saw-tooth curve bounded by the lines $y = x/4$ and $y = -x/4$. The lines forming the teeth of the saw all have slopes of 1 or -1, which means that they make angles of $45°$ with the x axis. Show that $\lim_{x \to 0} f(x) = 0$.

Solution. Having chosen an $\epsilon > 0$, let the lines $y = \epsilon$ and $y = -\epsilon$ be drawn, forming an ϵ band. Take $\delta = 4\epsilon$. Then, for $|x| < \delta$ it is clear that the boundary lines $y = x/4$ and $y = -x/4$ lie within

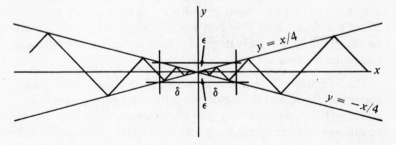

Figure   4.5

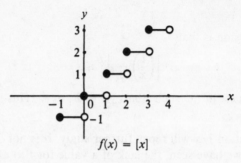

Figure 4.6

the ϵ band and hence the curve $y = f(x)$ does also. Since ϵ can be as small as we please, it follows that $\lim\limits_{x \to 0} f(x) = 0$.

The interesting feature of this function is that its graph crosses the x axis an infinite number of times in the neighborhood of the origin, and hence the graph cannot be drawn completely. Nevertheless $f(x)$ has a definite limit as $x \to 0$.

Example 3. The symbol $[x]$ stands for the greatest integer that is not greater than x (See Ex. 4, p 26) A part of its graph is shown in Figure 4.6. The graph consists of a set of horizontal line segments of unit length, in each of which the left-hand end, shown as a solid dot, belongs to the graph and the right-hand end, shown as a hollow dot, does not belong. Does $\lim\limits_{x \to 1} [x]$ exist?

Solution. The graph shows that, in a neighborhood to the left of $x = 1$ the value of $[x]$ is 0 and in a neighborhood to the right of $x = 1$, $[x]$ is 1. If an ϵ band in which $\epsilon < \frac{1}{2}$ were drawn, centered about $y = 0$ or about $y = 1$, it would not contain all the points on the graph in a δ interval, no matter how small δ were chosen. Hence $\lim\limits_{x \to 1} [x]$ does not exist.

This example will bear further study. If an ϵ band were drawn about the x axis, and if a δ band were bounded by the lines $x = 1$ and $x = 1 - \delta$, where $\delta < 1$, then the condition for a limit would be satisfied, the variable x being restricted to the points to the left of $x = 1$. We shall say that a *left-hand limit* exists and equals 0.

The symbol used is

$$\lim_{x\to 1^-} [x] = 0.$$

Similarly, a **right-hand limit** exists and equals 1;

$$\lim_{x\to 1^+} [x] = 1.$$

Example 4. Show that $\lim_{x\to 0} \sin(\pi/x)$ does not exist.

Solution. The graph of $y = \sin(\pi/x)$ is sketched in Figure 4.7. Since $\sin(\pi/x)$ has no value > 1 and none < -1, a limit, if it exists, must lie in the closed interval from -1 to 1. Choose any number L in this interval and let us require that $\sin(\pi/x)$ differ from L by not more than 0.9. This means that

$$\epsilon = 0.9,$$

a fairly large tolerance. Now $\sin(\pi/x)$ vanishes for

$$x = 1, \frac{1}{2}, \frac{1}{3}, \frac{1}{4}, \cdots \quad \text{and also for} \quad x = -1, -\frac{1}{2}, -\frac{1}{3}, -\frac{1}{4}, \cdots$$

Between any two consecutive vanishing points, the curve either rises to $y = 1$ or falls to $y = -1$. Hence, no matter how small a number δ is chosen, there will always be values of x in the interval

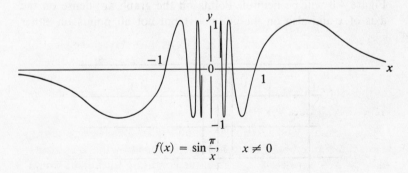

$$f(x) = \sin\frac{\pi}{x}, \quad x \neq 0$$

Figure 4.7

$-\delta < x < \delta$ for which $\sin(\pi/x) = -1$ and values for which $\sin(\pi/x) = 1$. Thus, for example, when

$$x = \frac{1}{\left(1000 - \dfrac{1}{2}\right)}, \quad \sin\left(\frac{\pi}{x}\right) = \sin\left(999\frac{1}{2}\right)\pi = -1,$$

and when

$$x = \frac{1}{\left(1000 + \dfrac{1}{2}\right)}, \quad \sin\left(\frac{\pi}{x}\right) = \sin\left(1000\frac{1}{2}\right)\pi = 1.$$

Hence the function does not remain within the required tolerance from L for any δ, however small. It follows that L is not a limit and, since L could be any number from -1 to 1, no limit exists. It should be noted, moreover, that neither a left-hand nor a right-hand limit exists.

Example 5. We raise now the question of a limit for an interesting but bizarre function. Given

$$f(x) = \begin{cases} 1, & \text{when } x \text{ is a rational number,} \\ 0, & \text{when } x \text{ is an irrational number,} \end{cases}$$

does $\lim\limits_{x \to 1} f(x)$ exist?

Solution. It is impossible to draw this graph satisfactorily though Figure 4.8 will be helpful. Points on the graph are dense on the axis of x and also on the line $y = 1$ but not all points on either

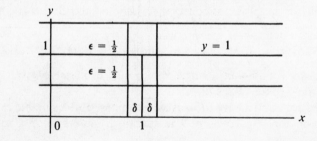

Figure   4.8

line belong to the graph. We have $f(1) = 1$. Is it possible that $\lim\limits_{x\to 1} f(x) = 1$? Taking $\epsilon = \frac{1}{2}$, let us draw an ϵ band around the line $y = 1$. Can we choose a δ band to match it? No matter how narrow we make the vertical δ band, there are points on the graph lying within the δ band that lie in the ϵ, δ rectangle and other points that do not. The condition for a limit is not satisfied. Neither for $x = 1$ nor for any other value of x has this function a limit.

Exercises

1. In finding $\lim\limits_{x\to 1} x^3$, a tolerance of ϵ is demanded for $|x^3 - 1|$. Show that a suitable tolerance for $|x - 1|$ is $\sqrt[3]{1 + \epsilon} - 1$.

2. The function $(x^2 + x)/x$ is not defined when $x = 0$. When $x \neq 0$, the function is equal to $x + 1$. Find $\lim\limits_{x\to 0} (x^2 + x)/x$.

3. Find $\lim\limits_{t\to 2} (t^2 - 4)/(t - 2)$ and justify your answer.

4. Sketch the graph of $f(x) = x^2 + 5x + 6$. State the value of $\lim\limits_{x\to -1} f(x)$ and support your statement by drawing ϵ and δ bands.

5. Find $\lim\limits_{x\to 0} \{(4 + x)^2 - 16\}/x$ and justify your answer.

6. Find $\lim\limits_{x\to \pi/2} \cos x$ by sketching a graph and employing ϵ and δ bands.

7. Find $\lim\limits_{x\to \pi/2} \sin x$ by sketching a graph and employing ϵ and δ bands.

8. In proving that $\lim\limits_{x\to 0} 2^x = 1$, a tolerance of $\epsilon = \frac{1}{1000}$ is demanded. Find a suitable matching value of δ.

9. Prove that if $f(x)$ is constant on an interval then $\lim\limits_{x\to r} f(x)$ exists at all points r of the interval.

10. Show that, if m and b are constants, $\lim\limits_{x\to k} (mx + b)$ exists for every k and that a single choice of δ to match a given ϵ will apply to all values of k.

11. When ϵ and δ have their usual meanings, find a suitable expression for δ in terms of ϵ in finding (i) $\lim\limits_{x\to 0} (5x + 3)/(x + 1)$, (ii) $\lim\limits_{x\to 1} (5x + 3)/(x + 1)$.

12. Sketch the graph of $f(x) = (2x + 1)/(x + 1)$. Show that (i) $\lim_{x \to 0} f(x) = 1$, (ii) $\lim_{x \to 1} f(x) = \frac{3}{2}$, (iii) $\lim_{x \to -1} f(x)$ does not exist.

13. It is given that $f(x) = 1$ when x is an integer and $f(x) = 0$ when x is not an integer. Show that $\lim_{x \to 2} f(x)$ exists and find its value.

4.6 An Important Limit

We consider

$$\lim_{x \to 0} \frac{\sin x}{x}$$

in which x is the radian measure of a variable angle. This limit is one of many in which the function, whose limit is desired, is a fraction whose numerator and denominator both tend to 0 at the point in question. Although the graph of $(\sin x)/x$ is not easily drawn, the graphs of the numerator and denominator (Figure 4.9) offer a clue to the limit. The two graphs are very close to coincidence in a small neighborhood of the origin. This suggests that $(\sin x)/x$ is very close to 1 or that $(\sin x)/x \to 1$ as $x \to 0$. We give a proof of this, based on the definition of a limit.

We take an acute angle whose measure, in radians, is x (Figure 4.10). With the vertex O as center, draw a circle of unit radius. The radii of the circle, OA and OP, are arms of the angle x radians. The remaining construction is clear from Figure 4.10. The radius

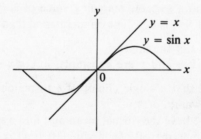

Figure   4.9

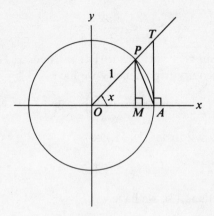

Figure 4.10

being 1, the measure of the arc AP is x and the measures of MP and AT are $\sin x$ and $\tan x$, respectively. The following inequality holds among areas:

$$\triangle OAP < \text{sector } OAP < \triangle OAT.$$

Since the areas of sectors of a circle are proportional to their arcs, the area of a sector with arc x units in a circle with radius r units is $x/2\pi r$ of the area of the circle. This gives

$$\frac{x}{2\pi r} \text{ of } \pi r^2 = \frac{1}{2}rx.$$

Since, in the circle of Figure 4.10, $r = 1$, the inequalities connecting the areas become

$$\frac{1}{2} \cdot 1 \cdot \sin x < \frac{1}{2} \cdot 1 \cdot x < \frac{1}{2} \cdot 1 \cdot \tan x,$$

from which

$$\sin x < x < \tan x. \tag{1}$$

Dividing by $\sin x$, which is positive, we get

$$1 < \frac{x}{\sin x} < \frac{1}{\cos x}$$

or

$$\cos x < \frac{\sin x}{x} < 1. \tag{2}$$

It follows that $(\sin x)/x$ is closer to 1 than is $\cos x$. How close is that? From elementary trigonometry we have

$$1 - \cos x = 2\sin^2\left(\frac{x}{2}\right) < 2\left(\frac{x}{2}\right)^2,$$

since $\sin(x/2) < x/2$, from (1). Hence

$$1 - \frac{x^2}{2} < \cos x. \tag{3}$$

By combining (2) and (3), we have

$$1 - \frac{x^2}{2} < \frac{\sin x}{x} < 1 \tag{4}$$

whence

$$0 < 1 - \frac{\sin x}{x} < \frac{x^2}{2}.$$

It is evident from these inequalities that the positive number $1 - (\sin x)/x$ can be made as small as we please by making x sufficiently small. The reader will find it an easy exercise to write a matching δ for any given ϵ.

One further step is necessary. In Figure 4.10 x is shown as positive. That this is not necessary can be seen from the fact that the inequalities (2) and (4) hold if $-\pi/2 < x < 0$, since

$$\cos(-x) = \cos x, \quad \frac{\sin(-x)}{-x} = \frac{\sin x}{x}, \quad \text{and} \quad \frac{(-x)^2}{2} = \frac{x^2}{2}.$$

Hence the conditions for a limit are satisfied, whether x is positive or negative. This completes the proof of the important formula

$$\lim_{x \to 0} \frac{\sin x}{x} = 1 \tag{5}$$

on which rests the whole structure of the application of calculus to the trigonometric functions.

We need to remind ourselves that *the variable x in* (5) *stands for the number of radians in the angle*. The fraction

$$\frac{\text{the sine of an angle}}{\text{the number of degrees in the angle}}$$

does not $\to 1$ as $x \to 0$. In fact, if x is the number of degrees in an angle, then the number of radians is $\pi x/180$. Hence

$$\lim_{x\to 0} \frac{\sin x}{\dfrac{\pi x}{180}} = 1 \qquad \text{or} \qquad \lim \frac{\sin x}{x} \cdot \frac{180}{\pi} = 1$$

and finally for an angle of x degrees,

$$\lim_{x\to 0} \frac{\sin x}{x} = \frac{\pi}{180}.$$

The inconvenience of this result, as compared to (5), explains why we speak of the radian as the natural unit for measuring angles. If a space vehicle from the earth were to drop some mathematics textbooks on Mars and if there were any Martian mathematicians who could decipher them, they might wonder why we divide 4 right angles into 360 units, but they would understand why we equate 4 right angles to 2π units (radians).

4.7 Two Extensions of the Definition of a Limit

The equation $xy = a^2$, where a is a nonzero constant, represents the relation between the pressure and the volume of a given mass of gas, according to Boyle's Law. The function defined by the equation, $y = a^2/x$, illustrates two significant modes of behavior of functions.

(1) As x increases without bound, a^2/x decreases and becomes "as close as we please" to 0. We shall write

$$\lim_{x\to\infty} \frac{a^2}{x} = 0.$$

(2) As x takes values closer and closer to 0, a^2/x increases without bound.

We write

$$\frac{a^2}{x} \to \infty \quad \text{as} \quad x \to 0 \quad \text{or} \quad \lim_{x \to 0} \frac{a^2}{x} = \infty,$$

We now clothe this argument in the strait-jacket of the ϵ, δ notation. (1) Suppose that the domain of $f(x)$ includes the part of the x axis to the right of some fixed point. If, given any small positive ϵ there exists a constant K so large that $|f(x) - L| < \epsilon$ for all values of $x > K$, then $f(x)$ tends to the limit L as x tends to ∞:

$$f(x) \to L \quad \text{as} \quad x \to \infty, \quad \text{or} \quad \lim_{x \to \infty} f(x) = L.$$

(2) If, given any positive number K, however large, there exists a matching positive number δ small enough so that $f(x) > K$ for all values of x for which $|x - a| < \delta$ then $f(x)$ tends to infinity (or becomes infinite) as x tends to a:

$$f(x) \to \infty \quad \text{as} \quad x \to a.$$

This last symbolism* is sometimes replaced by

$$\lim_{x \to a} f(x) = \infty.$$

Since any mathematical symbols mean only what they are defined to mean, we may use this latter symbolism as shorthand for the definition. It should, however, be used with caution. It seems to say that $f(x)$ approaches a limit which is equal to ∞. What it means is very different, namely, that (i) $f(x)$ approaches no limit as x tends to a, and (ii) for values of x sufficiently close to a, the values of $f(x)$ are very large, the set of these values being unbounded. This symbolism is a historical relic, inasmuch as in it the symbol ∞ does not stand for a number and the sign $=$ does not have its usual

---

*It is possible, and sometimes desirable, to discriminate between two modes of "becoming infinite". If $|f(x)| \to \infty$ while $f(x)$ remains positive, we shall write $f(x) \to +\infty$ and, if $|f(x)| \to \infty$ while $f(x)$ remains negative, we write $f(x) \to -\infty$. The following examples, expressed in the limit notation, are easily verified and illustrate the use of this definition:

$$\lim_{x \to +\infty} 2^x = +\infty; \quad \lim_{x \to -\infty} 2^x = 0; \quad \lim_{x \to 1^+} \frac{1}{x-1} = +\infty; \quad \lim_{x \to 1^-} \frac{1}{x-1} = -\infty.$$

meaning. It seems better, in order to avoid the temptation to read improper meanings into the parts of the symbolism, to use instead the first form given, with arrows instead of equality signs.

Example 1. Find the value of

$$\lim_{x \to \infty} \frac{2x + 3}{3x - 1}.$$

Solution. It is intuitively clear that, when x is very large, the constants 3 and -1 are of little weight compared with $2x$ and $3x$. In other words, the ratio of $2x + 3$ to $3x - 1$, when x is very large, differs little from the ratio of $2x$ to $3x$. This ratio is $\frac{2}{3}$.

We can now verify this conclusion as follows. Take $x \neq 0$; then

$$\frac{2x + 3}{3x - 1} = \frac{2 + \dfrac{3}{x}}{3 - \dfrac{1}{x}}.$$

As x increases, $3/x$ and $1/x$ decrease and can be made as small as we like by increasing x. It follows that

$$\lim_{x \to \infty} \frac{3}{x} = 0 \quad \text{and} \quad \lim_{x \to \infty} \frac{1}{x} = 0.$$

Hence

$$\lim_{x \to \infty} \left(2 + \frac{3}{x} \right) = 2, \quad \lim_{x \to \infty} \left(3 - \frac{1}{x} \right) = 3, \quad \text{and} \quad \lim_{x \to \infty} \frac{2x + 3}{3x - 1} = \frac{2}{3}.$$

This method, of dividing numerator and denominator by a suitable power of x, can be used with many rational functions.

4.8 The Limit of the Sum of Two Functions and Related Limits

It seems hardly necessary to prove that, since $\lim_{x \to 2} 3x^2 = 12$ and $\lim_{x \to 2} 5x = 10$, then $\lim_{x \to 2} (3x^2 + 5x) = 22$. If, however, you pause to ask yourself how this follows from the definition, you will realize that it requires a few steps of proof.* Fortunately, these steps are easily given.

THEOREM. *If* $\lim\limits_{x \to a} u(x) = A$ *and* $\lim\limits_{x \to a} v(x) = B$, *then* $\lim\limits_{x \to a} (u(x) + v(x))$ $= A + B$.

Proof. Since $\lim\limits_{x \to a} u(x) = A$, then to a positive number ϵ corresponds a positive δ_1 such that

$$|u - A| < \epsilon \qquad \text{whenever} \qquad |x - a| < \delta_1.$$

Since $\lim\limits_{x \to a} v(x) = B$, then to the same ϵ corresponds a positive δ_2 such that

$$|v - B| < \epsilon \qquad \text{whenever} \qquad |x - a| < \delta_2.$$

Now take δ to be the smaller of δ_1 and δ_2. Then, given $|x - a| < \delta$, we have both $|u - A| < \epsilon$ and $|v - B| < \epsilon$. It follows that

$$\begin{aligned} |u + v - (A + B)| &= |(u - A) + (v - B)| \\ &\leq |u - A| + |v - B| \\ &< 2\epsilon. \end{aligned}$$

The numbers δ_1 and δ_2 were originally chosen to match the number ϵ. The last inequality suggests that we now revise our choices. Instead of the original margin of ϵ we use the narrower margin of $\epsilon/2$ and let δ_1 and δ_2 be the matching δ's; these may need to be smaller than the first choices. Now, if δ is the smaller of the revised δ_1 and δ_2, we have that, given $\epsilon > 0$, a δ has been found so that

$$|u + v - (A + B)| < \epsilon \qquad \text{for} \qquad |x - a| < \delta.$$

It follows that

$$\lim\limits_{x \to a} (u + v) = A + B = \lim\limits_{x \to a} u + \lim\limits_{x \to a} v.$$

*If you are inclined to think of $\lim (u + v) = \lim u + \lim v$ as obvious, ask yourself what other mathematical operators obey this law. Does $(u + v)^2 = u^2 + v^2$? $\sqrt{u + v} = \sqrt{u} + \sqrt{v}$? $\sin (u + v) = \sin u + \sin v$? $\log (u + v) = \log u + \log v$? $2^{u+v} = 2^u + 2^v$? Does it not seem that $\lim (u + v)$ represents an exceptional operation indeed?

This can be stated briefly in the form: *the limit of the sum of two functions is the sum of their limits*

Various extensions of this theorem will suggest themselves. It extends to the sum of any finite number of functions.* Also, related theorems apply to the difference, product, or quotient of two functions, with the proviso for a quotient that the limit of the denominator is not zero. (See Exercises 22, 23, 24, p. 67)

Example 1.

$$\text{Lim}_{x \to 2} (3x^2 - 5x) = \lim_{x \to 2} 3x^2 - \lim_{x \to 2} 5x = 3 \lim_{x \to 2} x^2 - 5 \lim_{x \to 2} x$$
$$= 3 \times 4 - 5 \times 2 = 2.$$

Example 2.

$$\text{Lim}_{x \to -1} \frac{4x - 3}{2x + 5} = \frac{\lim (4x - 3)}{\lim (2x + 5)} = \frac{-4 - 3}{-2 + 5} = -\frac{7}{3}.$$

Example 3.

$$\text{Lim}_{x \to 2} (x^2 - 2x + 2)^4 = \left\{ \lim_{x \to 2} (x^2 - 2x + 2) \right\}^4$$
$$= (\lim_{x \to 2} x^2 - 2 \lim_{x \to 2} x + 2)^4 = (4 - 4 + 2)^4 = 16.$$

4.9   Continuous and Discontinuous Functions

This is a subject about which a student very early comes to have an intuitive concept. A function whose graph can be traced without taking the pencil off the paper is surely continuous. On the other hand a graph with a break or a jump represents a function that is discontinuous for the value of the independent variable at which the break occurs. These statements, of course, do not constitute a mathematical definition. In the concept of a limit we have now the means of replacing our feeling about continuity by an exact definition. Consider the two following examples.

*Not to an infinite series of functions, but that is another story.

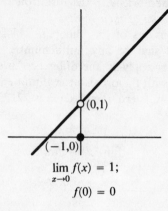

$$\lim_{x \to 0} f(x) = 1;$$
$$f(0) = 0$$

Figure 4.11

Example 1.

$$f(x) = x + 1 \qquad \text{when} \quad x \neq 0,$$
$$f(0) = 0.$$

It is readily proved for this function that $\lim_{x \to 0} f(x) = 1$. Since, however, $f(0) = 0$, the function has, as it were, a sudden jump from 1 to 0 (Figure 4.11). The fact that at $x = 0$ the value of the function is not equal to its limit creates a *discontinuity* in the function at this point.

Example 2.

$$f(x) = \begin{cases} x, & \text{for } x < 1, \\ x + 1, & \text{for } 1 < x, \end{cases} \quad f(1) \text{ is undefined.}$$

For this function (Figure 4.12)

$$\lim_{x \to 1^-} f(x) = 1 \qquad \text{and} \qquad \lim_{x \to 1^+} f(x) = 2.$$

The function is discontinuous at $x = 1$.

These two examples differ in an important respect. If, in Example 1, the definition of the function at $x = 0$ were changed from $f(0) = 0$ to $f(0) = 1$, the resulting function would be continuous.

In Example 2, no definition of the function at $x = 1$ would make it continuous.

DEFINITION. *A function* $\{(x, f(x))\}$ *whose domain includes the point a is continuous at this point if* $\lim_{x \to a} f(x)$ *exists and is equal to* $f(a)$.

This means that a function $\{(x, f(x))\}$ is continuous at a point if and only if

(*i*) $f(x)$ has a value at the point,
(*ii*) $f(x)$ has a limit as x tends to that point,
(*iii*) the limit of $f(x)$ is equal to its value.

It follows that the function $\{(x, f(x))\}$ can be discontinuous at a point for any one of three reasons:

(*i*) $f(x)$ is not defined at that point;
(*ii*) $f(x)$ has no limit at that point;
(*iii*) although $f(x)$ has both a value and a limit at the point, these are not equal.

Continuity, as just defined, can be described as a point concept; a point is first specified, then continuity or the lack of it is determined for this point. We now make an obvious extension of the idea to any point set. *A function is continuous over a point set if and only if it is continuous at every point of the set.* The point sets that are of

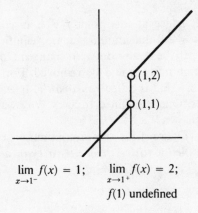

$$\lim_{x \to 1^-} f(x) = 1; \qquad \lim_{x \to 1^+} f(x) = 2;$$
$$f(1) \text{ undefined}$$

Figure 4.12

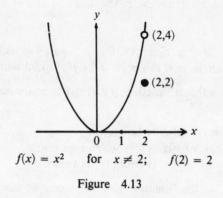

$$f(x) = x^2 \quad \text{for} \quad x \neq 2; \quad f(2) = 2$$

Figure 4.13

most interest in this connection are intervals on the number line. The following examples exhibit the most common kinds of discontinuity.

Example 3.

$$f(x) = x^2 \quad \text{when} \quad x \neq 2; \quad f(2) = 2. \text{ (Figure 4.13)}$$

This function is continuous for all values of x except $x = 2$. At $x = 2$ we have

$$\lim_{x \to 2} f(x) = 4$$

whereas $f(2) = 2$; hence at this point $f(x)$ is discontinuous. The discontinuity at $x = 2$ is due an unfortunate definition of the function at this point. If the definition were changed from $f(2) = 2$ to $f(2) = 4$, the discontinuity would be removed. For this reason, a discontinuity of this kind is called *removable*. It seems to have an artificial character. One is inclined to ask "Why was the function ever defined in this way?".

In Example 2 (Figure 4.12) the discontinuity at $x = 1$ is not removable. It is called a *finite discontinuity* or a *finite jump*.

Example 4.

$$f(x) = \frac{1}{x^2}, \, x \neq 0 \text{ (Figure 4.14)}$$

This function has at $x = 0$ neither a value nor a limit. The lack of a value, resulting from the fact that $1/x^2$ has no meaning when $x = 0$, can be remedied by an arbitrary definition, for example, $f(0) = 0$. However, no value assigned to $f(0)$ can make the function continuous at $x = 0$. The function is said to have an *infinite discontinuity* at this point.

Example 5.

$$f(x) = \sin\left(\frac{\pi}{x}\right), \ x \neq 0$$

This function has already been considered and its graph sketched (Figure 4.7, p. 51). The function is undefined and hence discontinuous at $x = 0$. The discontinuity differs in character from that of either of the last two examples. Instead of becoming infinite or approaching right and left limits, the function oscillates between 1 and -1 infinitely often in the neighborhood of $x = 0$.

Exercises /A

1. Give, without proof, the value of (i) $\lim_{x \to 2} (5x - 4)$, (ii) $\lim_{x \to 0.01} 1/x^2$, (iii) $\lim_{x \to 0} 8^x$, (iv) $\lim_{\theta \to \pi/3} \sec \theta$.
2. State the values of the following limits and illustrate by drawing ϵ and δ bands: (i) $\lim_{x \to 1} (4 - x^2)$, (ii) $\lim_{x \to -1} (x + 1)/x$.
3. Given that $f(x) = x^2$ when $x < 1$ and $f(x) = x$ when $x > 1$,

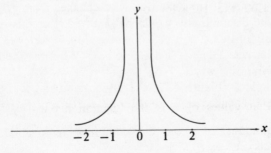

Figure 4.14

sketch the graph of $y = f(x)$ and investigate $\lim\limits_{x \to 1} f(x)$ by drawing ϵ and δ bands.

4. Given $f(x) = \frac{1}{2}(x + 3)$ when $x < 1$ and $f(x) = 4 - x$ when $x > 1$, draw the graph of $y = f(x)$ and investigate $\lim\limits_{x \to 1} f(x)$ by drawing ϵ and δ bands.

5. In order to prove that $\lim\limits_{x \to 3} (x - 2)^{-1} = 1$, a margin of ϵ is proposed. Show that a δ to match this ϵ must satisfy $1 + \epsilon \geqq (1 - \delta)^{-1}$ and $1 - \epsilon \leqq (1 + \delta)^{-1}$. Hence show that a suitable δ is $\epsilon/(1 + \epsilon)$. (*Hint*: Indicate on a graph the ϵ and δ bands.)

6. In order to prove that $\lim\limits_{x \to 2} (x^2 - x) = 2$, a margin of ϵ is proposed. Show that a δ to match this ϵ must satisfy $2 - \epsilon \leqq (2 - \delta)^2 - (2 - \delta)$ and $2 + \epsilon \geqq (2 + \delta)^2 - (2 + \delta)$. Show that $\epsilon/4$ is a suitable choice for δ. (*Hint:* Indicate on a graph the ϵ and δ bands.)

7. Calculate $\lim\limits_{x \to \infty} \dfrac{5 - 2x}{3 + x}$.

8. Calculate $\lim\limits_{x \to \infty} \dfrac{4x^2 - 5x + 2}{2x^2 + 3x - 4}$.

9. Calculate $\lim\limits_{x \to \infty} \dfrac{x + 1}{x^2 + 1}$.

10. Describe the behavior of $\dfrac{x^3 + 3x}{x^2 + 1}$ as $x \to \infty$.

11. Describe the behavior of $\dfrac{9}{x^2 - 9}$ as (i) $x \to 3^-$, (ii) $x \to 3^+$, (iii) $x \to -3^-$, (iv) $x \to -3^+$.

12. Describe the behavior of $\dfrac{x + 1}{x^2 + 3x - 10}$ as (i) $x \to 2^-$, (ii) $x \to 2^+$.

Exercises /B

13. For what values of x is the function defined by $\dfrac{3 + 2/x}{1 + 3/x}$ discontinuous? Are the discontinuities removable? Justify your answer.

14. In what respect do the functions defined by $x - 1$ and $(x - 1)^2/(x - 1)$ differ? Have these functions the same limit as $x \to 1$?

15. Given that $f(x) = (a_0 x^n + a_1 x^{n-1} + \ldots + a_n)/(b_0 x^n + b_1 x^{n-1} + \ldots + b_n)$, where $b_0 \neq 0$ and $b_n \neq 0$, state the value of (i) $\lim\limits_{x \to 0} f(x)$, (ii) $\lim\limits_{x \to \infty} f(x)$.

16. The function defined by $\dfrac{x^2 - 1}{x - 1}$ has a discontinuity in the domain of positive numbers. Give the reason for this and show that the discontinuity is removable.

17. From the relation $\lim\limits_{x \to 0} \dfrac{\sin x}{x} = 1$, show that $\lim\limits_{x \to 0} \dfrac{\sin^2(x/2)}{x^2} = \dfrac{1}{4}$.

18. Draw the graph of $y = |2x - 3|$. Show, by the use of ϵ and δ bands, that this function is continuous for $x = \frac{3}{2}$.

19. As $x \to \infty$, for what integral values of n does $x^n/(x^3 + x^2)$ tend to a limit? For what value of n is the limit different from 0? For what integral values of n does the function tend to ∞?

20. Show that the function for which $f(x) = 1$ when x is a rational number and $f(x) = 0$ when x is an irrational number is *completely discontinuous*, that is, it is continuous at no point.

21. Prove that $|u + v| \leqq |u| + |v|$ and $|u - v| \leqq |u| + |v|$.

22. Given that $\lim\limits_{x \to a} v(x) = B$, prove that $\lim\limits_{x \to a} (-v(x)) = -B$.

23. Given that $\lim\limits_{x \to a} u(x) = A$ and $\lim\limits_{x \to a} v(x) = B$, prove that
$$\lim\limits_{x \to a} (u - v) = A - B.$$

24. With the hypothesis of Exercise 23, prove that $\lim\limits_{x \to a} uv = AB$.

Chapter V | The Role of Limits In Infinite Series

5.1 From Sequence to Series

We begin with an example. The sequence

$$\left(\frac{1}{2^{n-1}}\right) \quad \text{or} \quad 1, \frac{1}{2}, \frac{1}{4}, \cdots, \frac{1}{2^{n-1}}, \cdots$$

has the limit 0 as $n \to \infty$. From this sequence we shall construct another, whose nth term is the sum of the first n terms of the first. The second sequence is

$$\left(1 + \frac{1}{2} + \frac{1}{4} + \cdots + \frac{1}{2^{n-1}}\right)$$

or

$$1, 1 + \frac{1}{2}, 1 + \frac{1}{2} + \frac{1}{4}, \cdots, 1 + \frac{1}{2} + \frac{1}{4} + \cdots + \frac{1}{2^{n-1}}, \cdots,$$

which we shall denote, for short, by (s_n) or by

$$s_1, s_2, s_3, \ldots, s_n, \ldots.$$

Then

$$s_n = 1 + \frac{1}{2} + \frac{1}{4} + \cdots + \frac{1}{2^{n-1}}.$$

Using the formula for the sum of n terms of a geometric progression, we find that

$$s_n = \frac{1 - \dfrac{1}{2^n}}{1 - \dfrac{1}{2}} = 2 - \frac{1}{2^{n-1}}$$

whence the sequence (s_n) can be written

68

Figure 5.1

$$1, \frac{3}{2}, \frac{7}{4}, \frac{15}{8}, \cdots, 2 - \frac{1}{2^{n-1}}, \cdots$$

It is easily proved that $\lim\limits_{n \to \infty} s_n = 2$ and the representation by points on the number line (Figure 5.1) illustrates this fact.

The equation $\lim\limits_{n \to \infty} s_n = 2$ is also written in the form

$$1 + \frac{1}{2} + \frac{1}{4} + \cdots + \frac{1}{2^{n-1}} + \cdots = 2.$$

The left member of this equation is an example of a new concept now to be defined.

DEFINITION. *Given a sequence $a_1, a_2, a_3, \ldots$, we make use of a new symbol*

$$a_1 + a_2 + a_3 + \ldots,$$

which is called an infinite series. This concept will receive further meaning in the developments that follow.

The terms of the sequence are also the terms of the infinite series. The series is distinguished from the sequence by the fact that the terms are connected by $+$ signs. When a particular series is given, it must be made clear how the terms can be continued without end.

An alternative symbol for this infinite series makes use of the **sigma notation** (Σ, sigma, is the Greek equivalent of S). This symbol is

$$\sum_{n=1}^{\infty} a_n$$

which, if the context makes the meaning clear, is sometimes abbreviated to

$$\sum_1^\infty a_n$$

or even to $\Sigma\, a_n$. Thus

$$\Sigma\, a_n = a_1 + a_2 + a_3 + \dots.$$

5.2 Convergence and Divergence of Infinite Series

As illustrated in the foregoing example, our study of the infinite series

$$a_1 + a_2 + a_3 + \dots$$

will be related to its *sequence of partial sums*

$$s_1, s_2, s_3, \dots,$$

where

$$s_n = a_1 + a_2 + a_3 + \dots + a_n.$$

We therefore direct attention to the variable s_n, *the sum of n terms of the series*, as n continues to increase, taking positive integral values. For the geometric series

$$1 + \frac{1}{2} + \frac{1}{4} + \cdots,$$

we saw that $s_n \to 2$ as $n \to \infty$. (Note that the method by which terms can be formed without end is here indicated by the words *geometric series*.)

DEFINITION. *If the sum s_n of the first n terms of an infinite series approaches a limit s as n becomes infinite, the series is said to* **converge** *or to be* **convergent** *and s is called the* **value** *of the infinite series. A series that does not converge is said to* **diverge** *or to be* **divergent**.

The following are examples of divergent series:
(a) $1 + 1 + 1 + \dots$, in which every term is 1. For this series $s_n = n$ and hence as *n* increases without limit, so does s_n;

(b) $1 + 2 + 3 + \ldots$, in which $s_n = n(n + 1)/2$ and therefore increases without limit;

(c) $1 - 1 + 1 - 1 + \ldots$, in which the terms have numerical value 1 but alternate in sign, the nth term being $(-1)^{n-1}$. For this series $s_n = 1$ when n is odd and 0 when n is even. Since s_n alternates between two distinct values, it does not tend to a limit and the series diverges.

5.3 A New Meaning for an Old Word

The value of a convergent infinite series is also called its *sum*. It is to be understood that this statement constitutes an extension of the meaning of the word *sum*. In the new sense of this word, the sum of the geometric series considered above is 2:

$$\sum_1^\infty \left(\frac{1}{2}\right)^{n-1} = 2,$$

although no one has ever added up all the terms of this series! The equation

$$\lim_{n \to \infty} s_n = s$$

for a convergent infinite series states that *the limit of a sum* (*in the old sense of this word*) *is equal to the sum of the series* (*in the new sense of sum*). In such ways does the terminology of mathematics burst its bounds! Think of the ways in which the word *number* has enlarged its meaning since the time when a number meant a positive integer! Until you are able clearly to distinguish between the two meanings of the word sum, it will be safer for you to speak of the *value* of a convergent series.

Although our attention will be confined mainly to convergent infinite series, this does not mean that all divergent series are "beyond the pale". Indeed, the sequence of partial sums s_1, s_2, s_3, ... is not the only sequence that repays study. It has already been seen (Exercise 15, p. 40) that, if all the numbers s_n are non-negative, the sequence

$$\left(\frac{s_1 + s_2 + \ldots + s_n}{n} \right)$$

is convergent if (s_n) is, and the two sequences converge to the same limit. Now take the series

$$1 - 1 + 1 - 1 + \ldots,$$

with alternating signs. This series was found to be divergent and so was ostracised, as it were, from the well-behaved family of series. For this series, $s_n = 1$ if n is odd and $s_n = 0$ if n is even. Hence the sequence

$$\left(\frac{s_1 + s_2 + \ldots + s_n}{n} \right) \quad \text{or} \quad \frac{s_1}{1}, \frac{s_1 + s_2}{2}, \frac{s_1 + s_2 + s_3}{3}, \ldots$$

is

$$1, \frac{1}{2}, \frac{2}{3}, \frac{2}{4}, \frac{3}{5}, \frac{3}{6}, \frac{4}{7}, \frac{4}{8} \ldots, \frac{n}{2n-1}, \frac{n}{2n}, \ldots$$

which is seen to converge to the limit $\frac{1}{2}$. So now why not make still another extension of the meaning of sum and restore the waif of a series: $1 - 1 + 1 - 1 + \ldots$ to respectability, with the "sum" $\frac{1}{2}$? This extension has been made and other series also have been rescued from ostracism in this way.

Finally, the question comes to mind: does the extension of the meaning of sum end here? The answer is no, further extensions have been made. The method used in every extension is to investigate a new *limit**. When the idea of limit was firmly rooted, it created a breach in the wall of the city of *Mathematics*, through which its artizans have set forth to blaze trails in many directions.

5.4 The Geometric Series

From surveying distant vistas, we return to earth now and to the subject of simple convergence. Consider the general geometric series

---

*If you wish to pursue this subject, you can begin with the Cesaro sum, which is illustrated above in the discussion of the series $1 - 1 + 1 - 1 + \ldots$.

$$a + ar + ar^2 + \ldots.$$

We take $a \neq 0$ and $r \neq 0$. If $r = 1$, $s_n = na$; then, as n increases, s_n increases in absolute value without limit and the series diverges. If $r \neq 1$,

$$s_n = a\,\frac{1 - r^n}{1 - r}$$

$$= \frac{a}{1 - r} - \frac{a}{1 - r}r^n. \tag{1}$$

Does s_n approach a limit as n increases? The answer depends upon r, as the following analysis shows.

If $r > 1$ or $r < -1$, the numerical value of r^n increases beyond all bounds. Suppose, for example, that $|r| = 1 + p$, where $p > 0$. Then

$$|r|^n = (1 + p)^n.$$

Since n is a positive integer, each of the $n + 1$ terms in the expansion of $(1 + p)^n$, by the binomial theorem, is positive. Hence the sum of all the terms exceeds the sum of the first two terms. Therefore

$$(1 + p)^n > 1 + np.$$

Since $p > 0$, $1 + np$ can be made as large as we please by making n large enough. Hence

$$|r|^n \to \infty \qquad \text{as} \qquad n \to \infty.$$

Suppose, on the other hand, that

$$-1 < r < 1, r \neq 0.$$

We wish to prove that

$$\lim_{n \to \infty} r^n = 0.$$

Let player A choose a positive number ϵ (for the purpose of the proof we ensure that $\epsilon < 1$). Then, to make his choice of an integer m, B reasons as follows:
We want

$$|r|^n < \epsilon.$$

Now set

$$|r| = \frac{1}{t}$$

where $t > 1$. Then we require

$$\frac{1}{t^n} < \epsilon$$

or

$$t^n > \frac{1}{\epsilon} > 1.$$

This last inequality is satisfied if

$$n > \frac{\log\left(\dfrac{1}{\epsilon}\right)}{\log t}.$$

The smallest integer that is greater than the positive number $\log\left(\dfrac{1}{\epsilon}\right)/\log t$ can be chosen as the integer m, to match the constant ϵ. Then

$$|r|^n < \epsilon \qquad \text{whenever} \quad n \geqq m.$$

It follows that

$$\lim_{n \to \infty} r^n = 0.$$

It is useful to reinforce, by some numerical examples, our conviction of the results that

      (i) if $|r| > 1$, then $|r|^n \to \infty$ as $n \to \infty$,

      (ii) if $|r| < 1$, then $\lim_{n \to \infty} r^n = 0.$

In contrast with

$$1^{100\,000} = 1,$$

we find that the number

$$(1 + 0.01)^{100\,000},$$

when expressed in decimal notation, has 433 digits to the left of

the decimal point, whereas
$$(1 - 0.01)^{100\ 000},$$

in decimal notation, has 435 zeros after the decimal point and before the first significant digit! These results can be verified with the use of a table of logarithms.

Two important conclusions now follow from (1):

(i) for $-1 < r < 1$, the geometric series $\Sigma\ a\ r^{n-1}$ converges;

(ii) its value, when it converges, is $\dfrac{a}{1 - r}$.

It may be noted that the geometric series can be recovered from the formula $\dfrac{a}{1 - r}$ by dividing $1 - r$ into a. This division, however, does not prove the convergence of the series or the validity of the formula. In fact we obtain

$$\frac{a}{1 - r} = a + ar + ar^2 + \ldots + ar^{n-1} + \frac{ar^n}{1 - r}.$$

This holds for all values of r except 1. If $r < -1$ or if $r > 1$, the **remainder term**

$$\frac{ar^n}{1 - r}$$

becomes extremely large numerically and is much the most important term in the expression on the right. If, on the other hand, $-1 < r < 1$, the remainder term dwindles away as n increases and gets closer and closer to 0. This throws light on the conditions of convergence and divergence of the series.

5.5   A Harmonic Series and its Generalization

The simplest harmonic series is the series of reciprocals of the natural numbers:

$$1 + \frac{1}{2} + \frac{1}{3} + \frac{1}{4} + \cdots \cdot \tag{1}$$

Allied to this are series such as

$$1 + \frac{1}{2^2} + \frac{1}{3^2} + \frac{1}{4^2} + \cdots$$

and

$$1 + \frac{1}{\sqrt{2}} + \frac{1}{\sqrt{3}} + \frac{1}{\sqrt{4}} + \cdots,$$

which are examples of the general series

$$1 + \frac{1}{2^p} + \frac{1}{3^p} + \frac{1}{4^p} + \cdots, \qquad (2)$$

in which p can stand for any real number.

Take first the harmonic series (1). Let us group the terms of this series, after the first, in groups of 1, 2, 4, 8, ... terms, thus:

$$1 + \left(\frac{1}{2}\right) + \left(\frac{1}{3} + \frac{1}{4}\right) + \left(\frac{1}{5} + \frac{1}{6} + \frac{1}{7} + \frac{1}{8}\right) + \cdots$$

In each group of terms the smallest term is the last. Hence the sum of the terms in the second group is $> 2(\frac{1}{4})$, which $= \frac{1}{2}$; the sum of the terms in the third group is $> 4(\frac{1}{8}) = \frac{1}{2}$, etc. Similarly, the sum of the terms in each group is $> \frac{1}{2}$. Since, in the infinite series, there is no end to the number of groups that can be formed and each group has a sum $> \frac{1}{2}$, therefore the sum of n terms of (1) can be made as large as we please by increasing n. The conclusion is that the harmonic series (1) is divergent.

This result, to one who meets it for the first time, is one of the most surprising facts in his mathematical experience. By adding terms of

$$1 + \frac{1}{2} + \frac{1}{3} + \frac{1}{4} + \cdots,$$

it is possible to get a sum greater than a billion! It must be remembered, however, that in order to get such a large sum the number of terms needed is enormous. For instance, the sum of 2000 groups is > 1000, but the number of terms in 2000 groups is

$$1 + 2 + 4 + \ldots + 2^{1999} = 2^{2000} - 1.$$

Pause for a minute and calculate how many digits this integer has when it is expressed in the decimal scale. (Use the fact that $\log 2 = 0.30103$)

Consider next the series (2):

$$1 + \frac{1}{2^p} + \frac{1}{3^p} + \frac{1}{4^p} + \cdots, \tag{2}$$

in which $p > 1$. The terms of this series, after the first, are smaller, respectively, than those of the harmonic series just considered. We adopt a different grouping of its terms, a grouping suggested by the conjecture that the series converges. The grouping is

$$(1) + \left(\frac{1}{2^p} + \frac{1}{3^p}\right) + \left(\frac{1}{4^p} + \cdots + \frac{1}{7^p}\right) + \left(\frac{1}{8^p} + \cdots + \frac{1}{15^p}\right) + \cdots.$$

In each parenthesis the largest term is the first. Hence the sum of the terms in the successive groups, after the first, are less, respectively, than

$$\frac{2}{2^p}, \frac{4}{4^p}, \frac{8}{8^p}, \cdots$$

The number of terms of series (2) that are contained in the first m groups is

$$1 + 2 + 4 + \ldots + 2^{m-1} = 2^m - 1.$$

Hence, if n is any number > 1 and $< 2^m$, the sum of n terms of (2) is less than the sum of m terms of

$$1 + \frac{1}{2^{p-1}} + \frac{1}{4^{p-1}} + \frac{1}{8^{p-1}} + \cdots.$$

This last is a geometric series with constant ratio $\frac{1}{2^{p-1}}$, whose sum to m terms is

$$\frac{1 - (1/2^{p-1})^m}{1 - (1/2^{p-1})} = \frac{2^{p-1}}{2^{p-1} - 1}\left(1 - \left(\frac{1}{2^{p-1}}\right)^m\right).$$

As $m \to \infty$ this partial sum approaches the limit

$$\frac{2^{p-1}}{2^{p-1} - 1}.$$

It follows that, as n increases, the sum of n terms of (2) increases monotonically and is bounded. Hence, by the theorem of p. 36, this sum approaches a limit. This completes the proof that (2) converges if $p > 1$.

When $p > 1$, the value of the series (2) is a function of p to which mathematicians have devoted some attention. It has been given the name the zeta (ζ) function:

$$\zeta(p) = \sum_{n=1}^{\infty} \frac{1}{n^p}.$$

5.6 Convergence and Divergence of Series

The two first questions that confront us in the study of infinite series are:

(i) Does the series converge?

(ii) If it converges, what is its value?

In what follows, we shall address ourselves to the first of these questions, only remarking that we shall often be able to show that a series converges although we can find only an approximation to its value.

5.61 *A necessary condition for convergence and a sufficient condition for divergence.* If the series

$$u_1 + u_2 + u_3 + \ldots$$

converges to the value s, then

$$\lim_{n \to \infty} s_n = s.$$

As $n \to \infty$, so also $n - 1 \to \infty$, whence

$$\lim_{n \to \infty} s_{n-1} = s.$$

Hence

$$\lim_{n \to \infty} (s_n - s_{n-1}) = s - s = 0,$$

which means that

$$\lim_{n \to \infty} u_n = 0. \tag{1}$$

Stated in words, this theorem says that, *if a series converges, its nth term approaches zero as n becomes infinite.* The condition (1) is therefore a *necessary* condition for convergence. However, one will burn his fingers, metaphorically, if he assumes that the condition is also sufficient. We have seen that

$$\sum_1^\infty \frac{1}{n}$$

is a divergent series whose nth term approaches zero.

It follows that, *if the nth term of an infinite series does not approach a limit as $n \to \infty$ or if it approaches a limit different from 0, the series diverges.*

It cannot be too strongly emphasized that **the condition**

$$\lim_{n \to \infty} u_n = 0$$

is necessary but not sufficient for convergence and that **the condition**

$$\lim_{n \to \infty} u_n \neq 0$$

is sufficient but not necessary for divergence. Now test yourself by answering the following questions and giving a series to illustrate each answer:

(1) If $\Sigma\, u_n$ converges, does it follow that $\lim_{n \to \infty} u_n = 0$?

(2) If $\lim_{n \to \infty} u_n = 0$, does it follow that $\Sigma\, u_n$ converges?

(3) If $\lim_{n \to \infty} u_n \neq 0$, does it follow that $\Sigma\, u_n$ diverges?

(4) If $\Sigma\, u_n$ diverges, does it follow that $\lim_{n \to \infty} u_n \neq 0$?

5.7 Direct Comparison Tests for Series of Positive Terms

The following two principles follow easily from the definition of convergence and their proofs will be omitted.

(a) *In testing any series for convergence, we may disregard any finite number of terms at the beginning of the series.*

(b) *The convergence or divergence of a series is not destroyed by multiplying every term of the series by the same nonzero constant.*

We consider now only series whose terms are all positive or zero. Such a series will be referred to as a *positive-term series*. In a positive-term series, the sum of n terms, s_n, is a monotone increasing function of n. If, then, s_n remains bounded, it must approach a limit and hence the series converges. On the other hand, if s_n is not bounded, then it must increase beyond all bounds and the series diverges.

For any unspecified convergent positive-term series, we shall use the notation

$$c_1 + c_2 + c_3 + \ldots$$

and for a divergent positive-term series

$$d_1 + d_2 + d_3 + \ldots .$$

Let

$$a_1 + a_2 + a_3 + \ldots$$

be a positive-term series to be tested. In the following tests, m denotes any properly chosen positive integer and the tests depend on the possibility of choosing this integer.

Test I. *If, for all values of $n \geqq m$, $a_n \leqq c_n$, the series Σa_n converges.*

Test II. *If, for all values of $n \geqq m$, $a_n \geqq d_n$, the series Σa_n diverges.*

Proofs. The proofs of these tests follow from the limit concept. In accordance with the principle (a) stated above, we disregard the first $m - 1$ terms of each series. Let s'_n denote the sum of n terms of Σa_n, *beginning with the mth term*, and let C'_n and D'_n denote the corresponding sums for Σc_n and Σd_n, respectively.

Under the conditions stated in Test I, $s'_n \leqq C'_n$. Since Σc_n converges, C'_n approaches a limit C' as $n \to \infty$. Moreover, for all values of n, $C'_n \leqq C'$, whence it follows that $s'_n \leqq C'$, a constant. Then, since the monotone increasing variable s'_n remains bounded, it approaches a limit. Hence Σa_n converges. Again, under the conditions stated in Test II, $s'_n \geqq D'_n$. Since D'_n is not bounded, s'_n is not bounded and approaches no limit. Hence Σa_n diverges.

Example 1. Test the series $\dfrac{1}{1} + \dfrac{2}{3} + \dfrac{3}{5} + \cdots + \dfrac{n}{2n - 1} + \cdots .$

Solution. The nth term of this series is

$$\frac{n}{2n - 1} = \frac{1}{2 - 1/n}.$$

It is easily proved that this term approaches the limit $\frac{1}{2}$ as $n \to \infty$. Since this limit is not zero, the series is divergent.

Example 2. Test the series $\frac{1}{2}\cdot\frac{1}{2} + \frac{2}{3}\cdot\frac{1}{4} + \frac{3}{4}\cdot\frac{1}{8} + \cdots$

$$+ \frac{n}{n + 1}\cdot\frac{1}{2^n} + \cdots.$$

Solution. We use for comparison the geometric series

$$\frac{1}{2} + \frac{1}{4} + \frac{1}{8} + \cdots,$$

which converges to the value 1. Since

$$\frac{n}{n + 1}\cdot\frac{1}{2^n} < \frac{1}{2^n},$$

each term of the given series is less than the corresponding term of the comparison series and since both are positive-term series, it follows that the given series converges. The value of the series is undetermined by this argument except that this value is between 0 and 1.

Example 3. Test the series $1 + \frac{1}{3} + \frac{1}{5} + \frac{1}{7} + \cdots + \frac{1}{2n - 1} + \cdots$

$$\tag{1}$$

Solution. The fact that we have found one harmonic series to diverge suggests that this harmonic series may also diverge. Hence we select a divergent series for comparison. The series

$$1 + \frac{1}{2} + \frac{1}{3} + \cdots$$

will not answer our purpose since the terms of the given series are not greater than the corresponding terms of this divergent series.

Making use of principle (b), we multiply the terms of this series by $\frac{1}{2}$, obtaining the divergent series

$$\frac{1}{2} + \frac{1}{4} + \frac{1}{6} + \cdots + \frac{1}{2n} + \cdots \tag{2}$$

Now, since

$$\frac{1}{2n - 1} > \frac{1}{2n},$$

it follows that every term of (1) is greater than the corresponding term of (2). Then, since (2) diverges and since all the terms of both series are positive, it follows that (1) diverges.

Exercises

Test the following series for convergence.

1. $1 + \frac{1}{2}\left(\frac{2}{3}\right) + \frac{1}{3}\left(\frac{2}{3}\right)^2 + \frac{1}{4}\left(\frac{2}{3}\right)^3 + \cdots + \frac{1}{n}\left(\frac{2}{3}\right)^{n-1} + \cdots$

2. $1 + \frac{1}{4} + \frac{1}{7} + \frac{1}{10} + \cdots + \frac{1}{3n - 2} + \cdots$

3. $1 + \frac{1}{\sqrt{2}} + \frac{1}{\sqrt{3}} + \frac{1}{\sqrt{4}} + \cdots + \frac{1}{\sqrt{n}} + \cdots$

4. $1 + \frac{1}{2\sqrt{2}} + \frac{1}{3\sqrt{3}} + \cdots + \frac{1}{n\sqrt{n}} + \cdots$

5. $\frac{1}{1.2} + \frac{1}{2.3} + \frac{1}{3.4} + \cdots + \frac{1}{n(n + 1)} + \cdots$

6. $\frac{1}{1^t} + \frac{1}{2^t} + \frac{1}{3^t} + \cdots + \frac{1}{n^t} + \cdots,$ for $0 < t < 1.$

7. $\sum_{1}^{\infty} \frac{2n}{3n - 2}$ 8. $\sum_{1}^{\infty} \frac{1}{4n - 3}$ 9. $\sum_{1}^{\infty} \frac{1}{n^2 + n}$ 10. $\sum_{1}^{\infty} \frac{n^2 - 1}{n^2 + 1}$

5.8 The Ratio Test

One of the useful series with which to test others by direct comparison of terms is the geometric series. We now transform the comparison with the geometric series into a simple test known as the ratio test. In the series

$$a_1 + a_2 + a_3 + \cdots$$

the ratio

$$\frac{a_{n+1}}{a_n} \quad \text{or} \quad \frac{a_n}{a_{n-1}}$$

will be called the *test-ratio*.

5.81   *First form of the ratio test*   Take all the terms of $\Sigma\, a_n$ to be positive.

> *If, for all values of $n \geqq m$, some fixed integer,*
>
> $$\frac{a_{n+1}}{a_n} \leqq r < 1,$$
>
> then the series $\sum a_n$ converges.

Proof.   We have

$$\frac{a_{m+1}}{a_m} \leqq r, \quad \text{whence} \quad a_{m+1} \leqq a_m r.$$

Also

$$\frac{a_{m+2}}{a_{m+1}} \leqq r, \quad \text{whence} \quad a_{m+2} \leqq a_{m+1} r \leqq a_m r^2.$$

Again

$$\frac{a_{m+3}}{a_{m+2}} \leqq r, \quad \text{whence} \quad a_{m+3} \leqq a_{m+2} r \leqq a_m r^3, \text{ and so on.}$$

It follows that each term of the given series, from the mth term on, is less than or equal to the corresponding term of the series

$$a_m + a_m r + a_m r^2 + a_m r^3 + \cdots.$$

Since $0 < r < 1$, this geometric series of positive terms converges. Hence, by the direct comparison test, $\Sigma\, a_n$ converges.

A corresponding test for divergence will be merely stated. Its proof offers no difficulty. *If, for $n \geqq m$, some fixed integer,*

$$\frac{a_{n+1}}{a_n} \geqq 1,$$

then $\Sigma\, a_n$ diverges.

One aspect of the sufficient condition for convergence that is embodied in the first form of the ratio test needs further emphasis. The condition requires that

$$\frac{a_{n+1}}{a_n} \leqq r, \quad \text{where} \quad r < 1,$$

for n greater than some fixed integer.

It is not sufficient that $\frac{a_{n+1}}{a_n} < 1.$

The validity of the test depends upon the existence of the number r that is itself less than 1. That the condition $a_{n+1}/a_n < 1$ is not sufficient for convergence is seen from the harmonic series

$$1 + \frac{1}{2} + \frac{1}{3} + \frac{1}{4} + \cdots$$

In this series the test-ratio is $n/(n + 1)$, which is < 1, but this series diverges. In other words, the fact that the nth term of a positive-term series decreases monotonically and approaches 0 as $n \to \infty$ does not imply that the sum of n terms approaches a limit. The unlimited number of the terms may overcome the effect of their extreme smallness.

5.82 *Second form of the ratio test.* Since the behavior of the test-ratio near the beginning of the series is of no importance, it is natural to examine how this ratio varies as n increases indefinitely. One important possibility is that the test-ratio may approach a limit. This leads to the following form of the ratio test for a series of positive terms.

If $\lim \frac{a_{n+1}}{a_n}$ *exists and* $= L$, *then*

if $L < 1$, $\sum a_n$ *converges,*

if $L > 1$, $\sum a_n$ *diverges,*

if $L = 1$, *the test fails to decide*

whether the series converges or diverges.

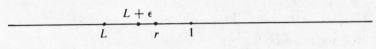

Figure 5.2

The advantage of this second form of the test is that it requires no bothersome number r. Its disadvantage is that even when the limit exists it may lead to no conclusion.

Proof. Suppose first that

$$\lim_{n \to \infty} \frac{a_{n+1}}{a_n} = L < 1.$$

Let r be any number between L and 1, so that $L < r < 1$ (Figure 5.2). Now in the game of limits let player A choose a number $\epsilon \leqq r - L$. Since

$$\lim_{n \to \infty} \frac{a_{n+1}}{a_n} = L,$$

it follows that player B can choose an integer m such that, for all $n \geqq m$, a_{n+1}/a_n differs from L by not more than ϵ. Hence $a_{n+1}/a_n \leqq r$ which is < 1, for $n \geqq m$. It follows from the first form of the ratio test that Σa_n converges.

Suppose, next, that

$$\lim_{n \to \infty} \frac{a_{n+1}}{a_n} = L > 1.$$

Then, if ϵ is taken $\leqq L - 1$, an m can be chosen such that, for all $n \geqq m$, a_{n+1}/a_n differs from L by less than ϵ and therefore by less than $L - 1$. (Figure 5.3). This means that $a_{n+1}/a_n > 1$ for all $n \geqq m$. Hence, by the first form of the test, Σa_n diverges.

Finally, suppose that $L = 1$. That the test in this case does not discriminate between convergent and divergent series is shown by the series

Figure   5.3

$$\frac{1}{1^p} + \frac{1}{2^p} + \frac{1}{3^p} + \cdots + \frac{1}{n^p} + \cdots, \quad p > 0.$$

Here the test-ratio is

$$\left(\frac{n}{n+1}\right)^p,$$

which, as $n \to \infty$, approaches the limit 1 for all values of p. However, this series converges if $p > 1$ and diverges if $p \leqq 1$.

Example 1. Test the series

$$1 + \frac{1}{2!} + \frac{1}{3!} + \cdots + \frac{1}{n!} + \cdots.$$

Solution. The test-ratio is

$$\frac{n!}{(n+1)!} = \frac{1}{n+1}$$

and

$$\lim_{n \to \infty} \frac{1}{n+1} = 0.$$

Hence, by the ratio test, the series converges.

Example 2. Test the series

$$\frac{1}{2.3} + \frac{2}{3.4} + \frac{3}{4.5} + \cdots + \frac{n}{(n+1)(n+2)} + \cdots.$$

Solution. The test-ratio is

$$\frac{n+1}{(n+2)(n+3)} \cdot \frac{(n+1)(n+2)}{n} = \frac{(n+1)^2}{n(n+3)}$$

$$= \frac{\left(1 + \dfrac{1}{n}\right)^2}{1 + \dfrac{3}{n}}.$$

It is apparent from this expression, and it is easily verified, that this ratio $\to 1$ as $n \to \infty$. Hence the ratio test fails to establish either convergence or divergence. We fall back, then, on a direct comparison test. It is well, in such a case, to take a critical look at the nth term in order to decide whether the series seems to converge or diverge. The harmonic series $\Sigma\, 1/(n + 2)$ is divergent. Now

$$\frac{1}{n + 2} = \frac{n}{n(n + 2)}$$

Since

$$\Sigma\, \frac{n}{n(n + 2)}$$

diverges, does it not seem likely that

$$\Sigma\, \frac{n}{(n + 1)(n + 2)}$$

will also diverge? Now select a divergent series for comparison. Since

$$\frac{n}{n + 1} > \frac{1}{2} \quad \text{if} \quad n > 1,$$

therefore

$$\frac{n}{(n + 1)(n + 2)} > \frac{1}{2(n + 2)} \quad \text{for} \quad n > 1.$$

But

$$\Sigma\, \frac{1}{n + 2}$$

diverges and hence

$$\Sigma\, \frac{1}{2(n + 2)}$$

diverges, by principle (b). Finally, the given series diverges.

Our purpose in this chapter has been to exhibit the fundamental role of limits in the study of infinite series rather than to make a systematic study of series. In the further study of convergence, a next step would be to investigate series whose terms are not all positive. For this and other topics, you are referred to treatises on advanced calculus or on infinite series.

Exercises

Test, for convergence, the following series.

1. $\dfrac{1}{1!} + \dfrac{2}{2!} + \dfrac{2^2}{3!} + \cdots + \dfrac{2^{n-1}}{n!} + \cdots$

2. $\dfrac{1}{1} + \dfrac{1}{1\cdot 3} + \dfrac{1}{1\cdot 3\cdot 5} + \cdots + \dfrac{1}{1\cdot 3\cdot 5\cdots(2n-1)} + \cdots$

3. $\dfrac{1}{10} + \dfrac{2!}{10^2} + \dfrac{3!}{10^3} + \cdots + \dfrac{n!}{10^n} + \cdots$

4. $\dfrac{2}{2} + \dfrac{3}{4} + \dfrac{5}{8} + \cdots + \dfrac{2^{n-1}+1}{2^n} + \cdots$

5. $1 + 2(1.01)^{-1} + 3(1.01)^{-2} + \ldots + n(1.01)^{-n+1} + \ldots$

6. $\dfrac{1\cdot 3}{2\cdot 4} + \dfrac{3\cdot 5}{4\cdot 6} + \dfrac{5\cdot 7}{6\cdot 8} + \cdots + \dfrac{(2n-1)(2n+1)}{2n(2n+2)} + \cdots$

7. $\displaystyle\sum_1^\infty \dfrac{2n-1}{(2n)^2}$ 　　 8. $\displaystyle\sum_1^\infty \dfrac{2n-1}{(2n)^3}$ 　　 9. $\displaystyle\sum_1^\infty \dfrac{(2n-1)(2n+1)}{(2n)^3}$

10. $\displaystyle\sum_1^\infty \dfrac{n+1}{n!}$ 　　 11. $\displaystyle\sum_1^\infty \dfrac{(1.001)^n}{n^3}$ 　　 12. $\displaystyle\sum_1^\infty \dfrac{n^2}{2^n}$

13. Show that, if the positive-term series $\displaystyle\sum_1^\infty a_n$ converges, then, given $\epsilon > 0$, an integer m exists such that $\displaystyle\sum_m^\infty a_n < \epsilon$.

14. Under what conditions can the convergence or divergence of the series $\Sigma\, a_n$ be asserted from the existence or non-existence of $\lim\limits_{n\to\infty} a_n$?

Chapter VI | An Important Limit: The Derivative

6.1 Introduction

It is a natural question to ask why a new mathematical method was needed and invented in the seventeenth century. While the emergence of genius is unpredictable, most great discoveries have a history extending back into earlier times. Two centuries earlier, the Renaissance had given rise to an immediate flowering of literature and the arts. The upsurge in science occurred somewhat later. It required the patient accumulation of data from experiment and observation before any great scientific syntheses could emerge.* The mathematical problems that had been considered up to that time could be described as mainly static problems; from certain known constants others were calculated. On the other hand, the phenomena that interested Newton were those involving change, such phenomena as winds and water currents, the ebb and flow of tides, chemical changes, and the motions of the sun, moon, and planets. For the mathematical treatment of these phenomena he found the older mathematics inadequate and he invented a mathematical instrument for investigating a dynamic world, a world in motion, or, to use his own word, a world in a state of flux.

More than once in the history of mathematics it has happened that a method has been introduced and used successfully although a strictly logical explanation of the method has had to wait for succeeding generations. A striking example of this was the inven-

---

*Two examples may be cited: (i) the laborious observations made by the astronomer Tycho Brahe, from which Kepler deduced his laws of planetary motion, which, in turn, formed the genesis of Newton's Law of Gravitation; (ii) the observations made by Galileo with his telescope, and his experiments with falling bodies, from the Leaning Tower of Pisa.

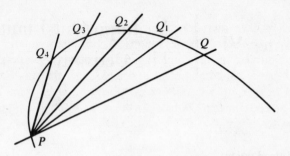

Figure   6.1

tion, in the seventeenth century, of the infinitesimal calculus, as it
was called, by Newton and Leibnitz. So successful was this in
providing solutions of interesting problems, that any logician
invited unpopularity by pointing out weaknesses in the explanations
then given. Bishop Berkeley (1685–1753) was such a logician, who
performed a notable service to mathematics by forcing the mathematicians of the eighteenth century to re-examine the foundations
of calculus. It was from this searching of foundations that the
doctrine of limits emerged.

As great a *tour de force* as the invention of calculus was, it had its
roots in problems that were handed down from ancient times. Of
these problems, two are of interest here. One is that of calculating
the *area bounded by a closed curve* such as the circle or ellipse, and
the *volume bounded by a closed surface*; the other is that of finding
the *tangent to a curve*. The latter problem will be considered in the
present chapter and the former problem in Chapter VII.

The problem of tangents is closely related to a physical
problem — that of finding *the instantaneous speed of a moving body*.
These problems, solved in the seventeenth century, foreshadowed
two main branches in the application of mathematical analysis, a
name applied to calculus and its developments. The problem of
tangents was the forerunner of the application of calculus to
geometry, now known as *differential geometry*. The problem of
speed led to the exact treatment of physical problems in what is
now *mathematical physics*.

Science has had many casualties in the·course of its history —
astrology and alchemy, to mention only two. In later days the

physicists have abandoned their *ether* and the mathematicians
their *infinitesimals* — those supposedly infinitely small but nonzero quantities. In this connection it has already been emphasized
that, if a point be chosen on a straight line, there is no next or
closest point to it. No matter how close to a given point a second
point be chosen, there is between them an interval comprising an
infinite set of points.

6.2   The Problem of Tangents

The niceties involved in this problem are somewhat obscured
for the beginner by the fact that for the first curve he studies — *the
circle* — the definition of a tangent can be given in an elementary
manner that does not generalize to other curves. A tangent to a
curve is a straight line that *touches* the curve at a *point of contact*;
this statement, of course, merely restates the problem without
suggesting a solution for it.

Let us begin with a point P on a curve and a straight line through
this point (Figure 6.1). We assume that this line cuts the curve in at
least one other point Q. On the arc PQ take a sequence of points
$Q_1, Q_2, Q_3, \ldots$ so that Q_1 is between P and Q, Q_2 is between P and
Q_1, and, in general, Q_{n+1} is between P and Q_n. This gives rise to a
sequence of secants: (PQ_n). We proceed to examine the behavior of
this sequence of secants as Q_n tends to P and to inquire what
feature may be common to all such sequences.

For this purpose we appeal to analytic geometry.* Suppose the
curve is defined, for a given domain of values of x, by an equation
$y = f(x)$ and let the coordinates of P be x_0 and y_0 (Figure 6.2).
The coordinates of Q differ from those of P and it is these differences that are crucial in our problem; in the figure, the directed
segment PR represents the difference of the abscissas and the
directed segment RQ represents the difference of the ordinates.

---

*It is one of the fortunate events in the history of science that Descartes' book
on Analytic Geometry appeared in 1637, five years before the birth of Newton.
One recalls Newton's remark that, if he had been able to see farther than other
men, it was because he stood on the shoulders of giants.

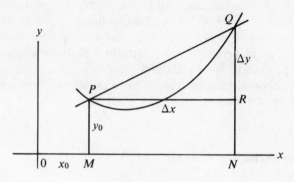

Figure   6.2

The symbols used for these differences are Δx and Δy; it is to be noted that Δx and Δy can be positive or negative and that Δy, but not Δx, can be 0. The symbol Δ is the Greek capital letter *delta*, corresponding to the modern *D*. Why do we not use *d* or *D*? This question has two answers: (i) *d* and *D* have been assigned other uses in the subject, (ii) the symbol Δ has been confirmed by three centuries of use. A difference between this use of symbols and that of algebra must be pointed out; Δx is not a product of two numbers but a single symbol, like the two syllables of a word. Thus, the square of Δx will be written $(\Delta x)^2$.

We are interested in the direction of the secant line PQ. This direction is designated by means of the *slope* of the line, which is the quotient RQ/PR or $\Delta y/\Delta x$. This ratio of differences or *difference quotient* is a function of Δx, where the domain of Δx is some interval surrounding but not including the point $\Delta x = 0$. Does the secant line PQ settle down to a "limiting" position as Q tends to P along the curve? A more precise form of this question is:

$$\text{Does } \lim_{\Delta x \to 0} \frac{\Delta y}{\Delta x} \text{ exist?}$$

If this limit does exist, it is called *the slope of the curve* at P and a line through P with this slope is the *tangent to the curve* at P. It may happen, at a specified point, that a curve has a tangent or that it has no tangent. While we are more familiar with *smooth* curves, a name by which we designate curves with tangents, it is easy to construct curves that, at certain points, are not smooth.

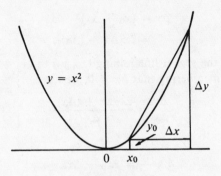

Figure 6.3

6.3 The Derivative as a Limiting Slope

We consider now the analytic steps involved in evaluating

$$\lim_{\Delta x \to 0} \frac{\Delta y}{\Delta x},$$

when this limit exists. Let us take for our curve the parabola whose equation is $y = x^2$ (Figure 6.3); essentially we are studying the *function* defined by $y = x^2$, whose domain may include the whole axis of x. We choose a definite value x_0 of x, for which y has the value y_0. Then

$$y_0 = x_0^2. \tag{1}$$

A neighboring point $(x_0 + \Delta x, y_0 + \Delta y)$ on the curve is obtained by adding to x an *increment* Δx and calculating the corresponding *increment* of y. The increment of x can be positive or negative but not zero.* We have

$$y_0 + \Delta y = (x_0 + \Delta x)^2. \tag{2}$$

---

*The necessity for taking $\Delta x \neq 0$ was not appreciated in the early days of the calculus. The instruction, in the final step of the differentiation process, to "let $\Delta x = 0$" was what, quite properly, aroused the scorn of Bishop Berkeley. See his essay "The Analyst" which is contained in *The Works of George Berkeley*, Vol. IV, pages 65–102 edited by A. A. Luce and T. E. Jessop, and published by Thos. Nelson & Sons Ltd., London. "The Analyst" was first published in 1734.

It follows, by subtraction, that

$$\Delta y = (x_0 + \Delta x)^2 - x_0^2$$
$$= 2x_0\Delta x + (\Delta x)^2. \tag{3}$$

The slope of the secant line joining (x_0, y_0) to $(x_0 + \Delta x, y_0 + \Delta y)$ is $\Delta y/\Delta x$. Remembering that $\Delta x \neq 0$, we have

$$\frac{\Delta y}{\Delta x} = \frac{2x_0\Delta x + (\Delta x)^2}{\Delta x}, \tag{4}$$

which reduces to

$$\frac{\Delta y}{\Delta x} = 2x_0 + \Delta x.$$

Now, by the process for finding a limit,

$$\lim_{\Delta x \to 0} \frac{\Delta y}{\Delta x} = 2x_0. \tag{5}$$

The number $2x_0$ that has been derived in the foregoing steps is the *derivative* of x^2 for the value x_0 of x. Since x_0 can be any real number, we can drop the subscript and say that the **derivative** of x^2, with respect to x, is $2x$. The phrase *with respect to x* reminds us of what the independent variable is. This becomes important in later developments. Equation (5) is now expressed, for any value of x, by

$$D_x x^2 = 2x$$

or, with the understanding that $y = x^2$, by

$$D_x y = 2x.$$

From the *function* defined by $y = x^2$, we have derived a second *function* defined by $y = 2x$. This second is the **derived function** or the **derivative** of the first. The process by which the derivative is obtained is called **differentiation**; in the foregoing example we have *differentiated* x^2.

6.4   The Derivative as a Limiting Speed

Suppose that a train starts from rest at a station and gains speed for several minutes. Suppose also that at a certain instant the

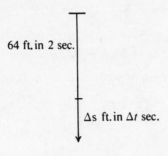

Figure 6.4

statement is made that the train is travelling at 40 miles per hour. What does this mean? Let us first dispose of some wrong answers. The statement does not mean that in the next hour the train will go 40 miles or that in the next quarter hour it will go 10 miles. In fact it does not mean that throughout any specified interval of time near the instant in question the train travels at 40 mph.

If, in *h* hours, the train travels *m* miles, at however variable a speed, we shall say that its *average speed* during the interval is *m/h* mph. If we calculate a sequence of average speeds during successively shorter *intervals* of time measured from a given instant, say 1 o'clock, it seems reasonable that these average speeds will get closer to the speed at 1 o'clock. But the speed at 1 o'clock is precisely what we want to define. It is clear that the limit concept comes once more to the rescue. *If the sequence of average speeds approaches a limit as the time interval tends to zero, this limit will be defined to be the instantaneous speed at the instant in question.*

Now, for an example, we consider a stone falling from rest (Figure 6.4). If, in *t* minutes, the stone falls *s* feet, then physics provides us with evidence that

$$s = 16t^2$$

very nearly.* Accepting this equation, let us find the speed of the stone at the end of 2 sec. In 2 sec the stone has fallen 64 ft and in $2 + \Delta t$ sec it has fallen

---

*If, at a point on the earth's surface, the acceleration due to gravity is *g* ft /sec / sec, then $s = \frac{1}{2}gt^2$. There are slight variations in *g* from point to point on the earth.

$$64 + \Delta s = 16(2 + \Delta t)^2$$

ft. This gives

$$\Delta s = 64\Delta t + 16(\Delta t)^2.$$

The average speed during Δt seconds is $\Delta s/\Delta t$ ft/sec, where

$$\frac{\Delta s}{\Delta t} = 64 + 16\Delta t.$$

It is now clear that

$$\lim_{\Delta t \to 0} \frac{\Delta s}{\Delta t} = 64$$

and, by our definition, the required speed at the instant when $t = 2$ is 64 ft/sec. In the symbolism of calculus, the value of $D_t s$, for the instant when $t = 2$, is 64.

Exercises

1. Find, by differentiation, the slope of the curve $y = x^3$ at the point (x, y) on the curve.
2. Show that the speed of the falling stone, when it has fallen for t seconds, is given by the formula $D_t s = 32\, t$.
3. From the results already obtained evaluate the derivatives $D_r r^2$, $D_x 5x^2$, $D_t k t^2$.
4. By carrying out the steps of the differentiation process, find $D_t 3t$ and $D_x c$, where c is a constant.
5. The curve formed by the cutting edge of a saw may be called a saw-tooth curve. Show why such a curve has no unique slope and hence no tangent at any one of its corners.
6. Indicate, on a suitably drawn curve $y = f(x)$, a segment on which, as x increases, $D_x y$ is (a) positive and increasing, (b) positive and decreasing, (c) negative and decreasing, (d) negative and increasing.

6.5   The Analytic Calculation of a Derivative

Guided by the two preceding examples, we now formulate the method of calculating a derivative. Let a function be defined by

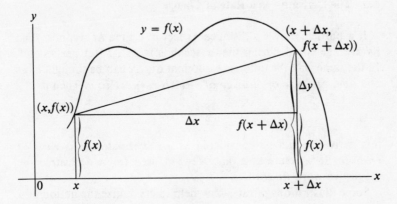

Figure 6.5

$y = f(x)$ on a continuous domain of values of x (Figure 6.5). In this domain, we specify a number x, which will remain fixed during the calculation. To x we add an *increment* Δx; this increment can be positive or negative. The range of values of $f(x)$ includes the number $f(x + \Delta x)$. We now form the **difference quotient**

$$\frac{\Delta y}{\Delta x} = \frac{f(x + \Delta x) - f(x)}{\Delta x},$$

which is a function of Δx. If this difference quotient approaches a limit as $\Delta x \to 0$, this limit is denoted by $D_x f(x)$ and is called the derivative, with respect to x, of $f(x)$.

In the process of finding the derivative of $f(x)$, the number chosen for x was held fast. Once the derivative is found, the need for this precaution disappears. Since x can be any point in the domain of the function, it follows that $D_x f(x)$ *defines a function of x.* The domain of this derived function is the set of all points in the domain of the original function for which the limit in question exists.

As an alternative notation, $D_x f(x)$ is denoted, for short, by $f'(x)$. If $y = f(x)$, this derivative is also denoted by y'. We can hardly go further in the abbreviation of the symbol.*

*Another notation for $D_x y$, not used in this book, is dy/dx.

6.6   The Derivative as a Rate of Change

If a particle moves a distance Δs feet in a time Δt seconds, then
its average speed during the Δt seconds is $\Delta s/\Delta t$ feet per second.
In the same way the difference quotient $\Delta y/\Delta x$ can be thought of as
the average rate of change of y with respect to x. Then if

$$\lim_{\Delta x \to 0} \frac{\Delta y}{\Delta x} = D_x y,$$

this derivative can be considered as *an instantaneous rate of
change.* It is interesting that Newton used for a derivative the
suggestive word *fluxion.*

Some illustrations of rates may help to crystallize the notion of a
derivative.

(*i*) If the barometric pressure at an altitude of x miles above the
earth is y pounds per square inch, then the rate of change of the
pressure with respect to the altitude can be expressed as $D_x y$
pounds per square inch per mile. This rate of change is called a
pressure gradient.

(*ii*) If the volume of a spherical balloon that is being inflated is V
cubic feet when the surface area of the balloon is S square feet,
then the rate of change of the volume with respect to the surface
is $D_S V$ cubic feet per square foot.

(*iii*) If the temperature at x inches from the hot end of an iron
poker is $T°$ C, then at that point the temperature is changing, with
respect to the distance along the poker, at the rate of $D_x T$ degrees
per inch. This rate is an example of a *temperature gradient.*

From the point of view of a derivative as a rate of change, it is
clear that the derivative of a constant is 0 and the derivative of x
with respect to x is 1; that is

$$D_x c = 0 \qquad \text{and} \qquad D_x x = 1.$$

Also the formula

$$D_x ku = k D_x u,$$

where k is a constant, is readily granted, since it seems clear that
the variable ku will change k times as fast as u. These results can,
of course, be deduced from the analytic rules.

Since a derivative is a limit, it shares the properties of limits. From the fact that

$$\lim_{\Delta x \to 0} \left(\frac{\Delta u}{\Delta x} + \frac{\Delta v}{\Delta x} \right) = \lim_{\Delta x \to 0} \frac{\Delta u}{\Delta x} + \lim_{\Delta x \to 0} \frac{\Delta v}{\Delta x},$$

it follows that

$$D_x(u + v) = D_x u + D_x v$$

and similarly that

$$D_x(u + v - w) = D_x u + D_x v - D_x w.$$

The symbol D_x, sometimes called an *operator*, is *distributive over the terms of a sum* and is one of the few common symbols in mathematics that are so distributive. (See footnote, p. 60)

Example.

$$\begin{aligned}
D_x(4x^2 - 5x + 6) &= D_x(4x^2) - D_x(5x) + D_x 6 \\
&= 4D_x x^2 - 5D_x x + D_x 6 \\
&= 4 \cdot 2x - 5 \cdot 1 + 0 \\
&= 8x - 5.
\end{aligned}$$

6.7 Maxima and Minima

Though it is not our purpose to set forth the details of the differential calculus, we cannot forbear to point out an elementary application that, of itself, would justify a study of the subject. If, at a point (x, y) on the curve $y = f(x)$,

$$D_x f(x) = 0,$$

then the tangent to the curve has, at this point, a slope of 0 and is therefore parallel to the axis of x. Such a point is called a **critical point**. The figures illustrate four possible cases. In Figure 6.6(a)

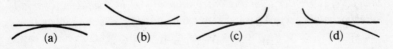

(a)   (b)   (c)   (d)

Figure 6.6

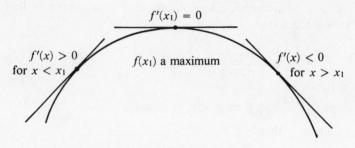

Figure   6.7

$f(x)$ attains, at the critical point, a maximum value, in 6.6(b) a minimum, and in 6.6(c) and 6.6(d), neither. In searching for a maximum
or a minimum of a function $f(x)$, the most useful tool is the derivative $f'(x)$. If it be granted that $f'(x)$ exists at a point, then a necessary
condition for a maximum or a minimum of $f(x)$ at the point is that
$f'(x) = 0$. Our first step, then, will be to find the critical points, if
any, by solving the equation

$$f'(x) = 0.$$

Figures 6.6(c) and 6.6(d) show that this condition is not sufficient.
To formulate sufficient conditions for a maximum, we examine
Figure 6.6(a). To the left of its critical point the slope of the curve,
$f'(x)$, is positive and, to the right, $f'(x)$ is negative. Similar conditions can be stated for a minimum.

Sufficient conditions for a maximum or a minimum of $f(x)$

If, at a point x_1 and in a neighborhood surrounding x_1 (Figure 6.7),

$$\text{(i)} \qquad f'(x_1) = 0,$$

(ii) $f'(x) > 0$ if $x < x_1,$

(iii) $f'(x) < 0$ if $x > x_1,$

*then $f(x_1)$ is greater than any other value of $f(x)$ in a sufficiently small
neighborhood of x_1. Again (Figure 6.8), if*

$$\text{(i)} \qquad f'(x_1) = 0,$$

(iv) $f'(x) < 0$ if $x < x_1,$

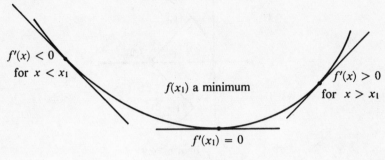

$f'(x) < 0$
for $x < x_1$

$f(x_1)$ a minimum

$f'(x) > 0$
for $x > x_1$

$f'(x_1) = 0$

Figure 6.8

(v) $f'(x) > 0$ if $x > x_1$,

then $f(x_1)$ *is less than any other value of $f(x)$ in a sufficiently small neighborhood of x_1.* At points outside the neighborhood mentioned, $f(x)$ can have greater or smaller values than $f(x_1)$. For this reason, $f(x)$ is called a *relative maximum* in the first case and a *relative minimum* in the second.

It remains to comment on Figures 6.6(c) and 6.6(d), in which $f(x)$ is not a maximum or a minimum at the critical point. On these curves $f'(x)$ has the same sign [positive in 6.6(c), negative in 6.6(d)] on both sides of the critical point. These are examples of *points of inflection;* at a point of inflection the tangent crosses the curve at its point of contact.

It may be pointed out that the physical, rather than the geometrical, genesis of a derivative would have led us to the same conclusions regarding maxima and minima. Thus, a maximum of $f(x)$ occurs at a point at which the rate of change of $f(x)$ is instantaneously zero whereas to the left of the point the function is increasing and to the right, decreasing. Thus do slopes and speeds merge in the problem of maxima and minima.*

---

*The importance of maxima and minima in engineering is readily appreciated. If engineers had an unlimited amount of material, time, and money, their problems would be much simplified. Many of their problems have to do with minimizing the expenditure of time, money, or materials, or of maximizing the stability of their structures or the efficiency of their machines.

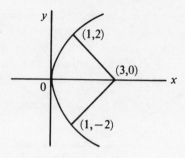

Figure   6.9

Example.   Find the points on the parabola $y^2 = 4x$ that are at the shortest distance from $(3, 0)$.

Solution.   Let A be the point $(3, 0)$ and let $P(x, y)$ be a point on the parabola (Figure 6.9). The problem requires that

$$PA = \sqrt{(x - 3)^2 + y^2}$$

should be a minimum. This is clearly equivalent to demanding that

$$(x - 3)^2 + y^2$$

be a minimum. Since x and y are related by the equation $y^2 = 4x$, then

$$(x - 3)^2 + y^2 = (x - 3)^2 + 4x$$
$$= x^2 - 2x + 9.$$

Applying the test for a minimum, we have

$$D_x(x^2 - 2x + 9) = 2x - 2,$$

which is 0 when $x = 1$. Also, when $x < 1$, $2x - 2 < 0$ and, when $x > 1$, $2x - 2 > 0$. This assures that $x = 1$ gives a minimum value of PA. When $x = 1$, $y = 2$ or -2. Hence the points $(1, 2)$ and $(1, -2)$ are the points required by the problem.

6.8   Asymptotes: An Application of Limits

In Chapter IV the equation $xy = a^2$ provided illustrations for two extensions of the use of limits. Geometrically the equation represents a rectangular hyperbola (Figure 6.10). If (x, y) is a point on the curve, then x and y are both positive or both negative; the curve lies in the first and third quadrants. Take the branch of the curve in the first quadrant. As x increases, y decreases and as x decreases, y increases. When x is large, the point (x, y) is close to the x axis. Now transform this into an exact statement: if a positive number ϵ is chosen as small as we please, then y will be $< \epsilon$ whenever $x > a^2/\epsilon$. This means that the distance from a point on the curve to the x axis approaches zero as $x \to \infty$. A description with less exactness but more warmth is that the curve hugs the x axis more and more closely as the point on it recedes farther and farther from the origin.

The relation of the x axis to the curve has a further characteristic. At the point (x, y) on the curve we have $y = a^2/x$. The slope of the tangent at this point is

$$y' = -\frac{a^2}{x^2}.$$

This slope is negative and approaches 0 as $x \to \infty$. Hence the direction of the tangent approaches the direction of the x axis as $x \to \infty$. Because of the two conditions just stated, the x axis is said to be an asymptote to the hyperbola.

DEFINITION: We consider a curve on which a point P varies so that its distance from any fixed point in the plane (the origin is a convenient point) becomes infinite. *A straight line is an asymptote*

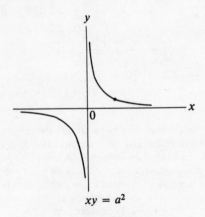

$$xy = a^2$$

Figure   6.10

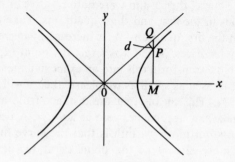

Figure 6.11

(or is asymptotic) to the curve if the following two conditions are satisfied:
  (1) *The distance of P from the line approaches zero;*
  (2) *The inclination of the tangent to the curve at P approaches the inclination of the line.**

Example. Show that the lines $bx - ay = 0$ and $bx + ay = 0$ are asymptotes of the hyperbola $b^2x^2 - a^2y^2 = a^2b^2$.

Solution. Consider the line $bx - ay = 0$ (Figure 6.11) and let an ordinate be drawn in the first quadrant, cutting the hyperbola in P and the line in Q. From the figure we have

$$PQ = MQ - MP = \frac{b}{a}x - \frac{b}{a}\sqrt{x^2 - a^2}$$

$$= \frac{b}{a}\left(\frac{x^2 - x^2 + a^2}{x + \sqrt{x^2 - a^2}}\right)$$

$$= \frac{ab}{x + \sqrt{x^2 - a^2}}.$$

*Intuitively, this means that, as a point tracing the curve moves farther and farther away, not only does the curve get closer and closer to its asymptote but also it lies flatter and flatter against the asymptote. A curve can be of an oscillatory character in which the oscillations lose their *amplitude* but not their *pitch*. Hence it is possible for the first condition stated in the definition to be satisfied without the second. For a discussion of this question and of "pseudo" asymptotes, see Berman and Stanton: Some Remarks on Asymptotes, *The Ontario Mathematics Gazette*, Vol. 1 December, 1962, Page 30.

If the distance from the point P to the line is d units, then, from the geometry of the figure, $d < PQ$, whence

$$d < \frac{ab}{x + \sqrt{x^2 - a^2}}.$$

Let us now demand that d be $< \epsilon$. This will be true if

$$x + \sqrt{x^2 - a^2} > \frac{ab}{\epsilon}$$

and, a fortiori, true if $x > ab/\epsilon$. Now take $K = ab/\epsilon$; then

$$d < \epsilon \quad \text{whenever} \quad x > K,$$

which means that

$$\lim_{x \to \infty} d = 0.$$

It has now been proved that condition (1) of the definition is satisfied. We turn to condition (2). The graph (Figure 6.11) provides strong evidence that the slope of the curve at P approaches the slope of the line as P moves farther and farther out on the curve. A rigorous proof of this fact requires the derivative of $\sqrt{x^2 - a^2}$. If the reader has difficulty in evaluating this derivative, he should refer to a textbook on calculus.

For a point (x, y) on the curve we have

$$b^2x^2 - a^2y^2 = a^2b^2$$

or, in the upper half-plane

$$y = \frac{b}{a}\sqrt{x^2 - a^2}.$$

The derivative of y is

$$D_x y = \frac{b}{a} \frac{x}{\sqrt{x^2 - a^2}}.$$

Now

$$\lim_{x \to \infty} \frac{b}{a} \frac{x}{\sqrt{x^2 - a^2}}$$

$$= \lim_{x \to \infty} \frac{b}{a} \frac{1}{\sqrt{1 - a^2/x^2}}$$

$$= \frac{b}{a}.$$

This means that the slope of the tangent to the curve approaches the slope of the line $bx - ay = 0$ as $x \to \infty$. Condition (2) is therefore satisfied.

It follows that the line $bx - ay = 0$ is an asymptote to the hyperbola in the first quadrant. From the symmetry of the curve, this line is also asymptotic to the curve in the third quadrant and the line $bx + ay = 0$ is asymptotic in the second and fourth quadrants.

The asymptotes of a curve, if any exist, form a sort of scaffolding that is useful in constructing the curve. In order that a curve have an asymptote it is necessary but not sufficient that it be not confined to the interior of any circle in the plane. The sinusoid, $y = \sin x$, is not so confined but it has no asymptote.

Exercises /A

1. By making use of the Binomial Theorem, show that, when n is a positive integer, $D_x x^n = n x^{n-1}$.
2. Find the derivative of (a) $5x^3 - 6x^2 + 4x - 3$,
   (b) $r^{2n} - 3r^n + 4$, (c) $(t^2 - 5)^2$.
3. Let x be a point in a domain in which $u(x)$ and $v(x)$ possess derivatives. An increment of Δx in x gives rise to increments in u and v. Denote these increments by Δu and Δv and, by completing the differentiation steps, prove that $D_x uv = u\, D_x v + v\, D_x u$.
4. Use the formula of Exercise 3 to calculate
   (a) $D_x(x^3 - 3)(2x^2 + 5x)$, (b) $D_x(x^2 + 3x)(4x^2 - 6x + 9)$.
5. Deduce from the formula of Exercise 3 that $D_x u^2 = 2u\, D_x u$.
6. Calculate (a) $D_r(r^2 - 4)^2$, (b) $D_t(5 + 6t - t^2)^2$.
7. Derive a formula for $D_x u^3$.
8. State, without proof, a formula for $D_x u^n$.

9. Prove, from first principles, the formula $D_x \frac{1}{x} = -\frac{1}{x^2}$ $(x \neq 0)$.

10. Find the value of x for which $2x^3 - 7x^2 - 12x + 8$ has (a) a relative maximum, (b) a relative minimum.

Exercises /B

11. Find the point on the curve $3y = (x - 3)(x^2 - 24)$ at which y has (a) a relative maximum, (b) a relative minimum.

12. A point moves on a straight line in such a way that its distance from a fixed point O of the line, at time t minutes after 1 o'clock, is $5t - 3t^2$ inches. Find (a) the velocity, (b) the acceleration of the point at the time when $t = 3$. Is the point approaching O or receding from it when $t = 3$?

13. Show that the x and y axes are both asymptotes of the curve $x^2y - x - 1 = 0$.

14. Beside a fenced field a rectangular plot of ground is to be enclosed, requiring fences on three sides. If 120 yards of fence are available, what should be the shape of the plot in order that it have a maximum area?

15. A closed cylindrical can is to be made to hold a given volume. Find the ratio of the height to the diameter of the can for the least surface area.

16. An open rectangular tank with a square base is to contain 1200 cubic feet. The bottom of the tank is to be constructed of material that costs one and a half times as much per square foot as that used in the sides. Find the most economical dimensions of the tank.

17. The surface area of a sphere is given by the formula $S = 4\pi r^2$. If the radius is measured in inches, and is increasing, find the rate of change of the surface with respect to the radius when $r = 3$, measured in square inches per inch.

18. Given that the postal regulations require that the sum of the length and girth of a parcel mailed may not exceed 72 inches, find the dimensions of the parcel of largest volume that can be mailed, the parcel being rectangular, with square cross section.

19. Find the points on the ellipse $x^2 + 4y^2 = 16$ that are at a minimum distance from $(1, 0)$.

20. Find the shortest distance from the point $(0, 4)$ to the hyperbola $x^2 - y^2 = 16$.

21. Show, from its graph, that the function defined by $y = |x - 1|$ has a minimum value at $x = 1$ but has no derivative at this point.

Chapter VII | Another Important Limit — The Definite Integral

7.1 Introduction

The discussion of infinite series in Chapter V was concerned with the limit of a sum as the number of its terms becomes infinite. The subject of this chapter is also the limit of a sum in which the number of terms becomes infinite but in which also each term approaches zero. Such limits arise from the problems on areas and volumes that were bequeathed to us by the ancient Greeks. We saw that *Eudoxus* and *Archimedes* had limited success with these problems. In the seventeenth century *Cavalieri* (1598–1647) returned to the problems with some fertile ideas. Finally, later in the same century, the problems received a definitive treatment in the *integral calculus* of *Newton, Leibnitz*, and their followers.

The area of a rectangle is determined by the product of the measures of its adjacent sides. A triangle has half the area of a rectangle with the same base and the same height. A polygon can be divided into triangles. So there is no difficulty in finding the areas of figures bounded by straight lines. These facts were enshrined in Euclid's Elements in the third century B.C. The problem that both fascinated and baffled the Greeks was that of determining the *areas of figures with curved boundaries*. Just as the fundamental rectilinear figure is the rectangle, so, in considering curvilinear figures, we shall begin with one that resembles a rectangle in having three straight sides and differs from it in having the fourth side curved. In the following discussion, we shall accept the intuitive, and hence naive, meaning of the word *area*. The definition of area must wait on the results of this discussion.

7.2 Approximations to an Area

Invoking the aid of analytic geometry, we consider a curve whose equation is $y = f(x)$ (Figure 7.1). We leave the function f unspecified

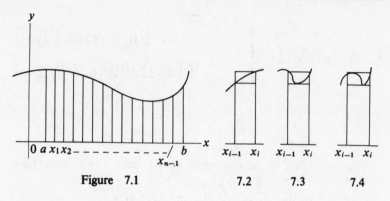

Figure 7.1   7.2   7.3   7.4

until we obtain some results that can be applied to specific functions. Take a portion of the curve $y = f(x)$ that is above the x axis and between the ordinates at $x = a$ and $x = b$. Consider the area bounded by the curve, the lines $x = a$ and $x = b$, and the x axis. We first divide this area into n strips by taking a set of $n - 1$ points $x_1, x_2, \ldots, x_{n-1}$, in order, between a and b. It would seem natural to take these points equally spaced, so that the distance between any two consecutive points is $(b - a)/n$; this is often convenient but it is not necessary and not always desirable. At each of the $n - 1$ points of division, erect an ordinate to the curve; these provide the n strips desired. Each strip resembles the whole area in having three straight segments and a curved segment in its boundary. The problem of finding the precise area of a strip is no different from, and therefore no easier than, that of finding the area of the whole figure. But let us not accept defeat so easily. Our intuition tells us that, if these strips are narrow enough, we can make a better job of approximating to the area of a strip than to that of the whole figure. It is this feeling about areas that mathematicians worked long to convert into precise mathematics.

Consider a particular one of these strips, that which lies between the ordinates at $x = x_{i-1}$ and $x = x_i$. We shall require of our curve that in this or in any interval it have a *minimum ordinate* and a *maximum ordinate*. These extreme ordinates, as we may call them, may be the vertical boundaries of a strip or they may not. Figures (7.2), (7.3), and (7.4) illustrate some possibilities. If, through the upper extremities of the extreme ordinates, parallels are drawn to the x axis, two rectangles are formed between which the area of the strip lies. This last statement is an assumption that is in accord with our feeling about areas.

We now need a bit of notation. Let $f(x_i')$ be the measure of the minimum ordinate of the strip, and $f(x_i'')$ the measure of the maximum ordinate. If the area of the strip is ΔA_i square units, we have

$$f(x_i')(x_i - x_{i-1}) \leqq \Delta A_i \leqq f(x_i'')(x_i - x_{i-1}).$$

The equality signs would apply in case the part of the curve at the top of the strip were a line segment parallel to the x axis. Now let this analysis be carried out for each of the n strips and the results summed. Then, denoting a by x_0, b by x_n and the required area $\sum_{i=1}^{n} A_i$ by A, we have

$$\sum_{i=1}^{n} f(x_i')(x_i - x_{i-1}) \leqq A \leqq \sum_{i=1}^{n} f(x_i'')(x_i - x_{i-1}). \qquad (1)$$

The sum on the left we shall call a *lower sum* s_n and that on the right an *upper sum* S_n, so that

$$s_n \leqq A \leqq S_n.$$

Now call on our intuition again. We feel that the curve would have to be a queer one indeed if, when the number of subintervals increases and the maximum length of a subinterval approaches zero, the difference between s_n and S_n does not approach zero as its limit. Since this point is crucial to our argument, let us suspend judgment while we accumulate a bit more evidence.

7.3   The Upper and Lower Sums

An open interval $h < x < k$, will be denoted, for brevity, by (h, k) and a closed interval, $h \leqq x \leqq k$, by $[h, k]$. Denoting $f(x_i')$ by m_i and $f(x_i'')$ by M_i, we have, for the function $f(x)$ and the interval $[a, b]$,

$$s_n = \sum_{i=1}^{n} m_i(x_i - x_{i-1}) \qquad \text{and} \qquad S_n = \sum_{i=1}^{n} M_i(x_i - x_{i-1}).$$

Hence

$$S_n - s_n = \sum_{i=1}^{n} (M_i - m_i)(x_i - x_{i-1}).$$

This measure of a piece of area through which the curve meanders (Figure 7.5) is reminiscent of the Method of Exhaustions of *Eudoxus* and *Archimedes*. Taking $a < b$, we have $x_i - x_{i-1} > 0$; also $M_i - m_i \geqq 0$. Hence

$$S_n - s_n \geqq 0.$$

Again, if M is the maximum value of $f(x)$ in the whole interval $[a, b]$, then $M_i \leqq M$ for all values of i and

$$S_n \leqq M \sum_{i=1}^{n} (x_i - x_{i-1}) = M(b - a).$$

For a similar reason, if m is the minimum value of $f(x)$ in $[a, b]$, then

$$s_n \geqq m(b - a).$$

These facts can be visualized in Figure 7.5.

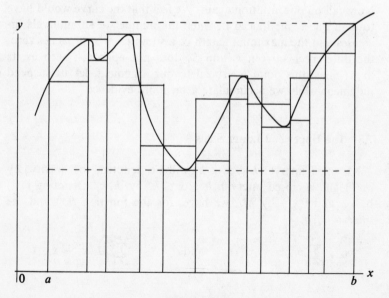

Figure   7.5

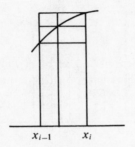

$$x_{i-1} \qquad x_i$$

Figure   7.6

All possible methods of subdivision of $[a, b]$ give rise to an
infinite set of values of s_n and of S_n, to all of which the inequalities
(1) apply. Beginning with a given subdivision, let us introduce
more points among the original points of division, thus forming a
more numerous set of subintervals. From a study of Figure 7.6,
in which a point of division is inserted between x_{i-1} and x_i, it is
clear that, if S_n is changed by the insertion of additional points,
it will be diminished. Similarly, if s_n is changed, it will be increased.
Now take two methods of subdivision, giving sums S', s' and
S'', s''. (We drop the subscript n, since the two methods may not
have the same number of subintervals.) Consider next the method
of subdivision that uses all the points of both the former methods.
Call the two sums for the combined subdivision $\bar{S}$ and $\bar{s}$. Then we
have

$$S' \geqq \bar{S} \geqq \bar{s} \geqq s'', \qquad \text{whence} \quad S' \geqq s''.$$

This means that every sum S, arising from whatever method of
subdivision, is at least as great as any sum s, arising from the same
or any other method of subdivision. Now if, beginning with some
initial subdivision, we continue to insert points so that the maximum length of a subinterval approaches 0, then the sum S will
decrease monotonically. Since, however,

$$S \geqq m(b - a),$$

the sum S is bounded below. It follows by the theorem of p. 36
that S *approaches a limit*, which we may call I'. Similar reasoning
shows that s *increases monotonically toward a limit*, which we
shall call I''.

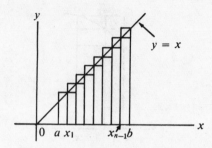

Figure   7.7

We have envisaged a sequence of subdivisions in which each one takes in all the points of subdivision of those preceding. More generally, we may consider any sequence of subdivisions in which the only requirement is that the maximum length of a subdivision approaches 0. It is plausible, but it requires a more refined proof, that all such sequences lead to the same upper and lower limits I' and I''. A proof is given in Appendix III.

Example 1. Apply the foregoing method to calculate the area enclosed by the straight line $y = x$, the x axis, and the lines $x = a$ and $x = b$.

Solution.   Figure 7.7 shows the area divided into strips; S_n measures the area under the upper stair-step curve and s_n the area under the lower. It will simplify the calculation to take the strips all of the same width, namely $(b - a)/n$ or Δx. Then

$$S_n = (x_1 + x_2 + \ldots + x_n)\Delta x$$
$$= (a + \Delta x + a + 2\Delta x + a + 3\Delta x + \ldots + a + n\Delta x)\Delta x$$
$$= \{na + \Delta x(1 + 2 + 3 + \ldots + n)\}\Delta x$$
$$= (n\Delta x)a + (\Delta x)^2\frac{n(n + 1)}{2}$$
$$= (n\Delta x)a + \frac{1}{2}(n\Delta x)^2 + \frac{1}{2}(n\Delta x)\Delta x.$$

Since $n\Delta x = b - a$, this becomes

$$S_n = (b - a)a + \frac{1}{2}(b - a)^2 + \frac{1}{2}(b - a)\Delta x$$

or $\qquad S_n = \frac{1}{2}(b^2 - a^2) + \frac{1}{2}(b - a)\Delta x.$

In a similar manner

$$
\begin{aligned}
s_n &= (x_0 + x_1 + \ldots + x_{n-1})\Delta x \\
&= (a + a + \Delta x + a + 2\Delta x + \ldots + a + \overline{n - 1}\Delta x)\Delta x \\
&= na\Delta x + (\Delta x)^2(1 + 2 + 3 + \ldots + n - 1) \\
&= a(n\Delta x) + \frac{1}{2}n(n - 1)(\Delta x)^2 \\
&= a(b - a) + \frac{1}{2}(b - a)^2 - \frac{1}{2}(b - a)\Delta x \\
&= \frac{1}{2}(b^2 - a^2) - \frac{1}{2}(b - a)\Delta x.
\end{aligned}
$$

As $n \to \infty$, $\Delta x \to 0$. Hence

$$
\lim_{n \to \infty} S_n = \lim_{n \to \infty} s_n = \frac{1}{2}(b^2 - a^2).
$$

What has been proved for this problem is that $I' = I''$, and we may call their common value I. It is natural to regard this as the measure of the area under the straight line and our conviction of this is reinforced by the fact that it agrees with the formula for the area of a trapezoid, which gives $\frac{1}{2}(b + a)(b - a)$.

Example 2. Take next the discontinuous function that was used earlier for another purpose:

$$
f(x) = \begin{cases} 0, & \text{when } x \text{ is a rational number,} \\ 1, & \text{when } x \text{ is an irrational number.} \end{cases}
$$

For this function, in the interval $[a, b]$, are the limits I' and I'' equal?

Solution. Divide the interval $[a, b]$ into n subintervals, as before (Figure 7.8). In any subinterval, no matter how short, the maximum value of $f(x)$ is 1 and the minimum value is 0. It follows readily that

$$
s_n = 0(b - a) = 0 \qquad \text{and} \qquad S_n = 1(b - a) = b - a.
$$

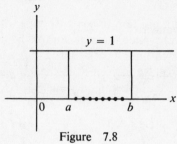

Figure   7.8

These sums are already constant and do not change as $n \to \infty$.
Hence

$$I' = b - a \qquad \text{and} \qquad I'' = 0.$$

For this function $I' \neq I''$.

DEFINITION.   *If, for a given function f and a given interval* $a \leqq x \leqq b$, *$I' = I''$, this common value is called the definite integral from a to b of* $f(x)$.

The symbol for this integral

$$\int_a^b f(x) \, dx,$$

derives from the symbolism of *Leibnitz*; the **integral sign** $\int$ is just the letter S grown up. If the integral exists, $f(x)$ is said to be **integrable from a to b**. In Example 1, the result is expressed by

$$\int_a^b x \, dx = \frac{1}{2}(b^2 - a^2).$$

In Example 2, on the other hand, the fact that $I' \neq I''$ is expressed by saying that the function is not integrable or that the integral does not exist.

7.4 The Area under a Curve: A New View of an Old Problem

We are now in a position to come to grips with the definition of area. We left in abeyance the meaning of the area bounded by a curve $y = f(x)$, two lines $x = a$ and $x = b$, and the x axis. The result we seem to have arrived at is that, if the area in question exists, its measure is the common value, I, of I' and I'', that is,

$$I = \int_a^b f(x)\, dx.$$

Let us now turn the tables on this troublesome concept of area. If the integral I exists, it is a definite number that we have a fair chance of calculating for a given function. *We shall define the measure of the area under the curve to be the value of this integral, when it exists.* If, for example, this integral has the value 10 and the unit of length is the inch, then the area under the curve is 10 square inches. The interesting fact emerges that, in order to define so apparently simple a concept as an area, we need the doctrine of limits.

7.5 The Fundamental Theorem of the Integral Calculus

It is not our purpose to explore the many facets of the definite integral. To do so would require a treatise on the integral calculus, and many such treatises exist. It is desirable, however, to pursue the subject farther in one direction in order to gather together two strands of thought that originated separately but became entwined in the seventeenth century.

7.51 *A matter of notation.* If $\int_a^b f(x)\, dx$ exists, consider the sums from which it arises:

$$S_n = \sum_{i=1}^n M_i(x_i - x_{i-1}) \qquad \text{and} \qquad s_n = \sum_{i=1}^n m_i(x_i - x_{i-1}).$$

Let us build a sum

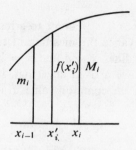

Figure   7.9

$$\sum_{i=1}^{n} p_i(x_i - x_{i-1}),$$

where $m_i \leqq p_i \leqq M_i$. This sum, if not equal to S_n or s_n, will lie in value between them and will therefore approach their common limit. It follows that, if x'_i is any point satisfying the inequality

$$x_{i-1} \leqq x'_i \leqq x_i$$

(Figure 7.9), then

$$\int_a^b f(x)\ dx = \lim \sum_{i=1}^{n} f(x'_i)(x_i - x_{i-1}).$$

In particular, x'_i can be taken as x_i or as x_{i-1}.

7.52   *The definite integral as a function of its upper limit.*   In Example 1, we found that

$$\int_a^b x\ dx = \frac{1}{2}(b^2 - a^2).$$

This result is independent of x. The variable x, which performed a role in giving existence to the integral, sacrificed its life in the process! The result would, in fact, have been the same if we had used any other symbol for the independent variable. Indeed this **variable of integration** is often called a "*dummy*" variable. So, for example,

$$\int_a^b f(x)\, dx = \int_a^b f(t)\, dt = \int_a^b f(\text{\textcurrency})\, d\text{\textcurrency} , \text{ and so on.}$$

So simple a device as this change of the variable of integration performs a useful service in some problems, as will now be illustrated. Let us keep in mind the area under the curve $y = f(x)$ as a focus for our ideas (Figure 7.10). Let x be any number between a and b [or any point in the interval (a, b)]. By using the interval $[a, x]$ in place of the interval $[a, b]$, we obtain $\int_a^x f(t)\, dt$. This integral, since it has a meaning for any x in the domain $[a, b]$, defines a new function F, where

$$F(x) = \int_a^x f(t)\, dt.$$

What properties has this function F? Taking a fixed value of x, let us add to it an increment Δx;

$$F(x + \Delta x) = \int_a^{x+\Delta x} f(t)\, dt.$$

From the meaning of an integral as the measure of an area, or as the limit of a sum, it follows that

$$F(x + \Delta x) = \int_a^x f(t)\, dt + \int_x^{x+\Delta x} f(t)\, dt$$

$$= F(x) + \int_x^{x+\Delta x} f(t)\, dt.$$

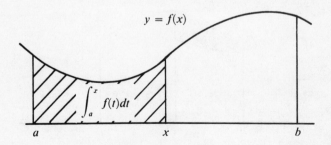

Figure   7.10

We have now to study the last-named integral. If m and M are the least and greatest values of $f(x)$ in the interval Δx, then

$$m\Delta x \leqq \int_x^{x+\Delta x} f(t)\, dt \leqq M\Delta x.$$

Hence

$$\int_x^{x+\Delta x} f(t)\, dt = \mu\Delta x,$$

where μ is a properly chosen number in the interval $[m, M]$. It follows that

$$F(x + \Delta x) - F(x) = \mu\Delta x. \tag{1}$$

If now $\Delta x \to 0$, μ remains bounded and $\mu\Delta x \to 0$. Hence

$$\lim_{\Delta x \to 0} F(x + \Delta x) = F(x).$$

This means that $F(x)$ is continuous at any point x in $[a, b]$ or, stated otherwise,

$$\int_a^x f(t)\, dt$$

is a continuous function of its upper limit x. The only requirement on the ***integrand*** $f(t)$ is that it be an integrable function in an interval $[a, b]$ containing x; it need not be continuous at all points. A consideration of Figure 7.11 will make clear that a small increment in x, *even at a point of discontinuity in $f(x)$,* will produce only a small increment in the area, that is, in $\int_a^x f(t)\, dt$.

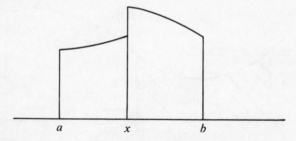

Figure   7.11

A more important result follows from (1) if we assume that $f(x)$ is a continuous function in the interval $[a, b]$. The difference quotient

$$\frac{F(x + \Delta x) - F(x)}{\Delta x} = \mu.$$

Remember that μ lies between m and M. Since $f(x)$ is continuous, then, as $\Delta x \to 0$, both m and M and therefore also μ approach the value $f(x)$. Hence

$$\lim_{\Delta x \to 0} \frac{F(x + \Delta x) - F(x)}{\Delta x} = \lim_{\Delta x \to 0} \mu = f(x).$$

This means that

$$F'(x) = f(x)$$

for any x in $[a, b]$. For this reason $F(x)$ is called a *primitive function* of $f(x)$, meaning a function whose derivative is $f(x)$.

It is clear that, if a function has a primitive function, it has many such functions. For,

$$if\, f(x) = D_x F(x),\; then\; also\; f(x) = D_x(F(x) + c)$$

for any constant *c. Suppose now that $F(x)$ is one primitive function of $f(x)$, namely,

$$F(x) = \int_c^x f(t)\, dt.$$

Then

$$F(b) = \int_c^b f(t)\, dt = \int_c^a f(t)\, dt + \int_a^b f(t)\, dt$$

as illustrated in Figure 7.12. Also

$$F(a) = \int_c^a f(t)\, dt.$$

---

*The converse of this theorem states that any two primitive functions of $f(x)$ differ at most by an additive constant. The proof, which is omitted here, will be found in any textbook on Calculus under the heading of The Theorem of Mean Value.

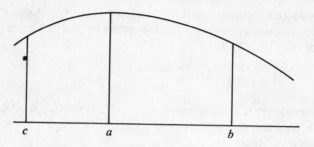

Figure   7.12

It follows that

$$F(b) - F(a) = \int_a^b f(t)\, dt.$$

The result contained in this formula is sometimes called the **Fundamental Theorem of the Integral Calculus.** It is worth while to pause to consider its significance. *The definite integral of $f(t)$ (or $f(x)$) with limits a and b is the difference between two values of any function that has $f(t)$ (or $f(x)$) for its derivative.* In this way, the integral calculus and the differential calculus join forces. The possibility of formulating the measure of an area, a volume, or other quantity as a limit of a sum was known to *Eudoxus, Archimedes*, and many later mathematicians. The problem that held them up was how to evaluate the limit that was involved. If, considering the area sketched in Figure 7.13, we take first 100 small strips, then 200 smaller strips, then 400 still smaller strips, and so on, then the evaluation of the successive approximations to the required area, and hence of their limit, poses an arithmetical problem that seemed

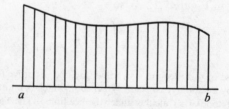

Figure   7.13

to have no feasible solution, It is true that some problems, such as $\int_a^b x \, dx$, yield to particular summation devices. The importance of the Fundamental Theorem, developed in the seventeenth century, is that, when

$$\lim_{n \to \infty} \sum_{i=1}^{n} f(x_i')(x_i - x_{i-1})$$

has been formulated as the answer to a problem, then the problem can be handed over to the differential calculus. *Can a function be found whose derivative is f(x)? If so, cease your worry about trying to sum millions of very small bits; simply take the difference between two values of a primitive function!* This theorem, in fact, resolved a flood of problems that had been awaiting solution for centuries.

Example 3.   Calculate the volume enclosed by a sphere with radius a units.

Solution.   Using rectangular axes, take a circle with center $(0, 0)$ and radius *a* units:

$$.x^2 + y^2 = a^2.$$

Let this circle generate the sphere by revolving about the x axis. Imagine the volume sliced by planes perpendicular to the x axis and consider a slice between the planes $x = x_{i-1}$ and $x = x_i$ (see Figure 7.14). Let x_i' be any point in the interval $[x_{i-1}, x_i]$ and let $y_i'^2 = a^2 - x_i'^2$. Then the measure of the volume of the sphere is given by

$$\lim_{n \to \infty} \sum_{i=1}^{n} \pi y_i'^2 (x_i - x_{i-1})$$

or

$$\lim_{n \to \infty} \sum_{i=1}^{n} \pi (a^2 - x_i'^2)(x_i - x_{i-1}).$$

This seems like a formidable limit. Its expression as an integral (see p. 118) is

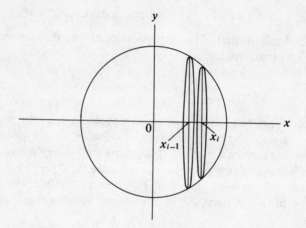

Figure   7.14

$$\int_{-a}^{a} \pi(a^2 - x^2) \, dx.$$

To evaluate this integral by using the Fundamental Theorem, we search for a primitive function of $\pi(a^2 - x^2)$. Such a function is seen to be $\pi \, (a^2x - x^3/3)$ since

$$D_x\pi(a^2x - x^3/3) = \pi(a^2 - x^2).$$

Hence the value of the integral is

$$\int_{-a}^{a} \pi(a^2 - x^2) \, dx = [\pi(a^2x - x^3/3)]_{x=a} - [\pi(a^2x - x^3/3)]_{x=-a}$$

$$= \pi(a^3 - a^3/3 + a^3 - a^3/3)$$

$$= \frac{4}{3}\pi a^3.$$

This is the familiar formula for the volume of a sphere.

It has been mentioned that many results in the differential and integral calculus were obtained before the underlying ideas of limits were thoroughly set forth. *Not all the building in the mathematical world has been done by beginning with the foundations!* This does not alter our appreciation of the power conferred by the doctrine of limits on the systematic development of the subject.

Exercises /A

Note: Assume the formula $D_x x^n = n x^{n-1}$, for all real values of n.

1. Give the meaning and the value of

$$\lim_{n \to \infty} \sum_{i=1}^{n} (x_i - x_{i-1})$$

where $x_0 = a$, $x_n = b$, and $a < b$.

2. Give the value of $\int_{-3}^{2} 10 \, dx$ and illustrate your answer by a diagram.

3. Formulate as the limit of a sum $\int_{0}^{2} x^2 \, dx$. Show on a diagram an area under the curve $y = x^2$ that this integral measures. Use the Fundamental Theorem to evaluate the integral.

4. Evaluate, by the Fundamental Theorem, $\int_{1}^{2} x^5 \, dx$.

5. Evaluate $\int_{-a}^{a} x^3 \, dx$ and explain the result.

6. Evaluate

$$\lim_{n \to \infty} \sum_{i=1}^{n} (1 + 2x_i)(x_i - x_{i-1})$$

where $x_0 = 0$ and $x_n = 10$.

7. Find, by integration, the area under the curve $y = 4 - x^2$ and above the x axis.

8. Evaluate

$$\int_{1/2}^{2} \frac{4}{x^2} \, dx.$$

9. Evaluate

$$\int_{-1}^{3} (x^2 - 5x + 4)\, dx.$$

10. Evaluate

$$\int_{1}^{4} t\sqrt{t}\, dt.$$

Excercises /B

11. Assuming that $D_x f(x) = \phi(x)$, evaluate $\int_{k}^{m} \phi(t)\, dt$.

12. Evaluate $\int_{0}^{1} (x^3 - x^2)\, dx$ and $\int_{1}^{2} (x^3 - x^2)\, dx$. Show by a diagram why one answer is negative and the other positive.

13. Formulate as the limit of a sum $\int_{0}^{\pi} \sin x\, dx$. Show, on a diagram, an area under the curve $y = \sin x$ that it measures.

14. Given that

$$\lim_{n \to \infty} \sum_{i=1}^{n} \alpha_i = \lim_{n \to \infty} \sum_{i=1}^{n} \beta_i = s$$

and that $\alpha_i \leqq \gamma_i \leqq \beta_i$ for $i = 1, 2, \ldots, n$, show that

$$\lim_{n \to \infty} \sum_{i=1}^{n} \gamma_i = s.$$

15. Calculate the volume of revolution generated when the area under the curve $y = x^3$ from $x = 0$ to $x = 2$ is revolved about the x axis.

16. Calculate the volume of revolution generated when the area under the curve $y = x^2$ from $x = -1$ to $x = 1$ is revolved about the x axis.

17. Formulate as the limit of a sum the measure of the area under the curve $y = 2^x$ from $x = -3$ to $x = 0$. Express this limit in the conventional form of a definite integral.

18. Evaluate

$$\lim_{n \to \infty} \sum_{i=1}^{n} \sqrt{x'_i}(x_i - x_{i-1}),$$

where $x_0 = 1$ and $x_n = 9$.

19. A function $f(x)$ for which $f(x) = f(-x)$ is called an **even function**. Examples of even functions are $\cos x$ and x^{2n}, where n is an integer. Show that, if $f(x)$ is an even function,

$$\int_{-a}^{a} f(x)\, dx = 2 \int_{0}^{a} f(x)\, dx.$$

20. A function $f(x)$ for which $f(x) = -f(-x)$ is called an **odd function**. Examples of odd functions are $\sin x$ and x^{2n-1}, where n is an integer. Show that, if $f(x)$ is an odd function,

$$\int_{-a}^{a} f(x)\, dx = 0.$$

Appendix I | The Set of Rational Numbers

We assume without definition the set I of integers; in what follows a single letter will stand for an integer. It is a part of our assumption that the integers are subject to the four rational operations of *addition*, *subtraction*, *multiplication*, and *division*, which obey the following laws:

for addition, the commutative law: $a + b = b + a$;

the associative law: $a + (b + c) = (a + b) + c$;

for multiplication, the commutative law: $ab = ba$;

the associative law: $a(bc) = (ab)c$;

for addition and multiplication, the distributive law:

$$a(b + c) = ab + ac.$$

The set of rational numbers will not be taken for granted, as the set I was, but defined in terms of the integers. We shall therefore make no more assumptions but give only definitions and deductions from these definitions.

Taking any two numbers a, b, of I, with the restriction noted in I below, we shall enlarge our number system by defining a pair of integers (a, b), in the order a, b to be a new "number" in an extended sense of this word. We proceed to assign properties to these new numbers, these properties being an essential part of their definition.

I. In (a, b) we specify that $b \neq 0$.

II. If $a = kb$, the number $(a, b) = k$. Hence $(a, 1) = a$ and $(0, b) = 0$. It follows that the new set of numbers includes the integers as a subset.

III. *Equality:* (a, b) is defined to be equal to (c, d) if and only if $ad = bc$. It follows that $(ma, mb) = (a, b)$ for all integral values of m except 0. The *form* in which a number is expressed is not unique since, for example, $(2a, 2b) = (3a, 3b)$.

128

IV. *Inequality:* $(a, b) > (c, d)$ if and only if one of the following conditions holds: (i) $ad > bc$; and $bd > 0$, (ii) $ad < bc$ and $bd < 0$; $(a, b) < (c, d)$ if and only if $(c, d) > (a, b)$.

V. *Addition:* $(a, b) + (c, d)$ shall mean $(ad + bc, bd)$.

Do the laws of addition, assumed for the set I, hold also for the new numbers? Since

$$(a,b) + (c,d) = (ad + bc, bd) = (cb + da, db) = (c,d) + (a,b),$$

the commutative law holds. Also

$$(a,b) + \{(c,d) + (e,f)\} = (a,b) + (cf + de, df)$$
$$= (adf + bcf + bde, bdf),$$

and

$$\{(a,b) + (c,d)\} + (e,f) = (ad + bc, bd) + (e,f)$$
$$= (adf + bcf + bde, bdf).$$

Hence the associative law of addition holds.

Does addition possess an inverse operation? The question of whether the number (c, d) can be subtracted from (a, b) is the question of whether a number (x, y) exists such that

$$(c,d) + (x,y) = (a,b).$$

This will be true if and only if x and y can be found such that

$$(cy + dx, dy) = (a,b).$$

that is if, for a suitable integer m,

$$cy + dx = ma$$

and

$$dy = mb.$$

A little observation suggests for m the value d^2. Then

$$cy + dx = d^2a$$
$$dy = d^2b,$$

whence $y = bd$ and $x = ad - bc$. Hence the difference

$$(a,b) - (c,d) = (ad - bc, bd).$$

VI. *Multiplication:* $(a, b) \times (c, d)$ shall mean (ac, bd).

With this definition, we examine the laws of multiplication. Since

$$(a,b) \times (c,d) = (ac,bd) = (ca,db) = (c,d) \times (a,b),$$

the commutative law holds. Also

$$(a,b) \times \{(c,d) \times (e,f)\} = (a,b) \times (ce,df) = (ace,bdf)$$

and

$$\{(a,b) \times (c,d)\} \times (e,f) = (ac,bd) \times (e,f) = (ace,bdf).$$

This verifies the associative law for multiplication. For the distributive law we have

$$(a,b) \times \{(c,d) + (e,f)\} = (a,b) \times (cf + de, df)$$
$$= (acf + ade, bdf).$$

Also

$$(a,b) \times (c,d) + (a,b) \times (e,f) = (ac,bd) + (ae,bf)$$
$$= (acbf + bdae, b^2df)$$
$$= (acf + dae, bdf)$$
$$= (acf + ade, bdf).$$

This verifies the distributive law.

Does multiplication possess an inverse operation? The question of whether there exists a number (a, b) divided by (c, d) is the question of whether (x, y) exists such that

$$(c,d) \times (x,y) = (a,b).$$

This will be true if and only if $(cx, dy) = (a, b)$, that is if

$$cx = ma \quad \text{and} \quad dy = mb,$$

for a suitably chosen m. Take for m the value dc. Then, provided $c \neq 0$ and $d \neq 0$, we have $x = ad$ and $y = bc$. We therefore conclude that

$$(a,b) \div (c,d) = (ad, bc).$$

The definition of (a, b) and (c, d) requires that $b \neq 0$ and $d \neq 0$.

The added requirement here that $c \neq 0$ means that the divisor (c, d) must not be 0.

VII. *Relation of the new numbers to the integers.* The numbers $(a, 1)$ and $(b, 1)$ are integers a and b, respectively. The equation

$$(b,1) \times (x,y) = (a,1)$$

is equivalent to the two equations $bx = pa$ and $y = p$, for some integer p. The value $p = b$ will make these equations true for $x = a$ and $y = b$. Hence

$$(b,1) \times (a,b) = (a,1).$$

It follows that (a, b) can be written as the quotient of two integers $(a, 1)/(b, 1)$ or a/b.

Our result is that the newly defined number can be expressed as a fraction or a ratio of integers. The four rational operations have been defined so that the results agree with the usual combinations of fractions. In particular we note the requirement that the denominator of the fraction be not zero.

In constructing the foregoing definitions, we were guided by the rules with which we are familiar in operating with fractions. The reason for this development is a matter of logic: if we assume without definition the existence and properties of the positive integers, then no more assumptions are necessary in defining the rational numbers. Logically, a rational fraction is a pair of integers satisfying certain rules of operation. To be sure, the satisfaction one gets from this fact is aesthetic rather than practical. We continue to use fractions as we first learned to do.

Appendix II | The Limit of a Bounded Monotone Sequence

Figure A.II. 1

THEOREM.   *A bounded, monotone increasing sequence of numbers approaches a limit.*

Let k be an upper bound of the monotone increasing sequence (s_n). Take a number h that is not an upper bound of (s_n). Then there are points of (s_n) between h and k. Bisect the interval $[h, k]$ by the point h_1. Either there are or there are not points of (s_n) to the right of h_1; if there are, bisect $[h_1, k]$, if there are not, bisect $[h, h_1]$. Call the last point of bisection found h_2. If h_2 is between h and h_1, then bisect $[h_2, h_1]$ or $[h, h_2]$, depending on whether there are or are not points of (s_n) to the right of h_2. Continue this process of bisection, obtaining a sequence of intervals, each with half the length of its predecessor and each having the property that there are points of (s_n) in the closed interval but none to the right of it. All of these closed intervals contain at least one point in common.

If the length of $[h, k]$ is l units, then the length of the nth interval of the sequence is $l/2^n$ units. As $n \to \infty$, $l/2^n \to 0$. Hence all the intervals cannot contain more than one point in common since, if they contained two points, they would contain the interval joining them and this would contradict the fact that the length of a subinterval $\to 0$. Hence there exists one and only one point m such that (i) no point of (s_n) is to the right of m and (ii) every point to the left of m has points of (s_n) to its right. It follows that $\lim_{n \to \infty} (s_n)$ exists and equals m.

Appendix III

The Limits of the Darboux Sums

(The symbols used below are defined on pages 111–113)

The upper and lower sums are sometimes called the Darboux sums. Take first a *positive* function $f(x)$ and an interval $[a, b]$ with $a < b$. A subdivision of $[a, b]$: $x_0(=a)$, x_1, x_2, ..., x_{n-1}, $x_n(=b)$, leads to a sum

$$S = \sum_{i=1}^{n} M_i(x_i - x_{i-1}).$$

We have $S \geqq m(b - a)$. Hence, for all methods of subdivision, the sums S are bounded below. Of all their lower bounds, there must be a greatest one. This *greatest lower bound* will be denoted by I'.

THEOREM OF DARBOUX. *In a subdivision of $[a, b]$ let the maximum length of a subinterval be η. If a set of such subdivisions is envisaged for which $\eta \to 0$, then $\lim_{\eta \to 0} S = I'$.*

Proof: The fact that I' is the greatest lower bound of the sums S means that, given any $\epsilon > 0$, there exists a subdivision for which

$$S < I' + \frac{\epsilon}{2}.$$

Suppose that the subdivision specified above has this property. Now take a second subdivision, finer than the first, in which the greatest subinterval is less than the smallest subinterval of the first subdivision. Let δ be chosen so that the maximum length of a subinterval, by this second method, is $< \delta$. Suppose that this second subdivision gives rise to the upper sum S'.

We separate the subintervals that contribute to the sum S' into two sets: I, those that do not contain any of the points x_1, x_2, ...,

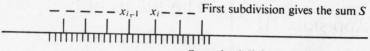

Second subdivision gives the sum S'

Figure A.III.1

x_{n-1}; II, the $n - 1$ subintervals that contain these points. (If a point x_i is a division point of the second subdivision, let the left subinterval p be included in I and the right subinterval q in II.)

Consider I. Since $f(x) > 0$, the contribution of a part of the subinterval $[x_{i-1}, x_i]$ is less than that of the whole subinterval. Hence, by summation, the contribution of all the subintervals specified in I is less than S and therefore $< I' + \epsilon/2$.

Consider II. This has $n - 1$ subintervals each of which contributes to S' an amount less than $M\delta$. The total contribution of II is therefore $< M\delta(n - 1)$. Now we have a criterion on which to base our choice of δ. Take

$$\delta < \frac{\epsilon}{2M(n - 1)};$$

then $M\delta(n - 1) < \epsilon/2$.

Hence the total sum S arising from I and II is less than $I' + \epsilon/2 + \epsilon/2$, that is

$$S < I' + \epsilon.$$

We have now matched the chosen ϵ with a δ such that

$$S - I' < \epsilon \qquad \text{whenever} \quad \eta < \delta.$$

It follows that $\lim_{\eta \to 0} S = I'$.

Similarly it can be proved that $\lim_{\eta \to 0} s = I''$.

The restriction was made that $f(x) > 0$. Suppose that $f(x)$ is not positive on the whole of $[a, b]$. Add to $f(x)$ a constant k so that $f(x) + k > 0$ in $[a, b]$. The theorem holds for $f(x) + k$, which means that

$$\lim_{\eta \to 0} (f(x) + k) = I'_1,$$

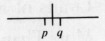

Figure A.III.2

say, and hence

$$\lim_{\eta \to 0} f(x) = I'_1 - k.$$

This is the limit I' of the theorem.

Appendix IV | Limits of Functions of More Than One Variable

The following discussion applies to functions of two variables. The generalization to functions of three or more variables offers little difficulty.

An *ordered triple* (x, y, z) of real numbers can represent a point in space of three dimensions. We consider a set of such triples, $\{(x, y, z)\}$ for which a correspondence exists, as follows: to any point (x, y) in a certain *domain* of points in the x, y plane, there corresponds one and only one number z. Such a set of triples is defined to be a *function*. The *domain* of the function is the set of points (x, y) and the *range* of the function is the set of values of z. x and y are called the *independent variables* and z the *dependent variable*. The function can be denoted by a single letter, such as f or F.

The *values of the function F* are defined to be the values of z and are denoted by $F(x, y)$. Thus, if the correspondence required by the function is set up by the equation $z = 2y - x$, then

$$F(x,y) = 2y - x$$

and, in conformity with conventional practice, we shall speak of the *function $2y - x$* and, similarly, of the *functions $x^2 + y^2$, $\dfrac{1}{x} - \dfrac{1}{y}$, $5x \cos 3y$*, to take three examples.

The question arises concerning the concept of a limit for a function of two variables; can a meaning be assigned, for example, to the symbol

$$\lim_{(x,y)\to(3,4)} (2y - x)?$$

The geometrical representation of

$$z = 2y - x,$$

136

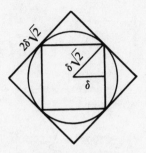

Figure A. IV. 1

as a *plane*, suggests that this "limit" should be assigned the number 5. To give meaning to this conjecture, we need first the concept of a *two-dimensional neighborhood* of the point $(3, 4)$. We may take a *square neighborhood*: $|x - 3| \leq \delta$, $|y - 4| \leq \delta$ or a *circular neighborhood*: $(x - 3)^2 + (y - 4)^2 \leq \delta^2$. Since a square with side 2δ can be inscribed in a circle with radius $\delta\sqrt{2}$, which, in turn, can be inscribed in a square with side $2\delta\sqrt{2}$, it is immaterial whether we use square or circular neighborhoods; in fact neighborhoods with other boundaries can be used when they are convenient.

To justify the statement that

$$\lim_{(x,y)\to(3,4)} (2y - x) = 5,$$

let us demand a margin ϵ for $|2y - x - 5|$. We then search for a corresponding positive margin δ such that

$$|2y - x - 5| \leq \epsilon$$

for *every* point (x, y) for which

$$(x - 3)^2 + (y - 4)^2 \leq \delta^2$$

If, for *any* given positive ϵ, such a margin δ can be found, we shall define that

$$\lim_{(x,y)\to(3,4)} (2y - x) = 5. \tag{1}$$

The proof of equation (1) can now be given. In order that

$$(x - 3)^2 + (y - 4)^2 \leq \delta^2$$

it is sufficient that

$$|x - 3| \leqq \frac{\sqrt{2}\delta}{2} \quad \text{and} \quad |y - 4| \leqq \frac{\sqrt{2}\delta}{2}.$$

Then

$$|2y - x - 5| = |2(y - 4) - (x - 3)|$$
$$\leqq 2|y - 4| + |x - 3|$$
$$\leqq \sqrt{2}\delta + \frac{\sqrt{2}\delta}{2} = \frac{3}{2}\sqrt{2}\delta.$$

We now choose δ so that

$$\frac{3}{2}\sqrt{2}\delta = \epsilon \quad \text{or} \quad \delta = \frac{\epsilon\sqrt{2}}{3}.$$

The condition for the limit, as stated in (1), is then satisfied.

The geometrical interpretation of equation (1) is a generalization of that for a function of one variable. In place of an ϵ band, we have an ϵ slice, consisting of the space between the horizontal planes $z = 5 - \epsilon$ and $z = 5 + \epsilon$. In place of the δ band, we can use a δ cylinder erected on the circle in the x, y plane:

$$(x - 3)^2 + (y - 4)^2 = \delta^2.$$

This equation of a circle in the x, y plane is also the equation of the cylinder (Figure A.IV.2.) in the space of x, y, z. The intersection of the cylinder with the slice gives a frustum of the cylinder with radius δ and length 2ϵ. The problem is to choose δ so that all points (x, y, z) on the plane $z = 2y - x$, that are within the δ cylinder, are also within the ϵ slice.

DEFINITION OF A LIMIT OF $f(x, y)$. *If a number L exists such that, given any positive ϵ, no matter how small, there exists a corresponding positive δ such that*

$$|f(x,y) - L| \leqq \epsilon$$

whenever

$$(x - a)^2 + (y - b)^2 \leqq \delta^2$$

(*or whenever*

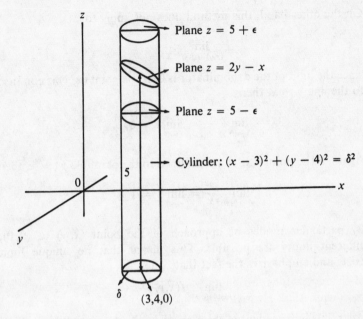

Figure A. IV. 2

$$|x - a| \leqq \delta, \quad \text{and} \quad |y - b| \leqq \delta)$$

then

$$\lim_{(x,y)\to(a,b)} f(x,y) = L.$$

The evaluation of limits by the ϵ, δ process often presents greater difficulty for functions of two variables than for functions of one variable. In some problems one relies on the geometrical evidence, illustrated above. Again, in some problems, the properties of limits of sums, products, and quotients (which are here assumed) lead to the desired results.

Example.

$$\lim_{(x,y)\to(1,2)} \frac{y^2}{x} = \frac{\lim_{y\to2} y^2}{\lim_{x\to1} x} = \frac{4}{1} = 4.$$

On the other hand, this method does not apply to

$$\lim_{(x,y)\to(0,0)} \frac{y^2}{x}$$

since the limit of the denominator is 0. If the point (x, y) is confined
to the line $y = x$, then

$$\lim_{\substack{(x,y)\to(0,0)\\y=x}} \frac{y^2}{x} = \lim_{x\to0} x = 0.$$

Again, if the points (x, y) are confined to the parabola $y^2 = x$, then

$$\lim_{\substack{(x,y)\to(0,0)\\y^2=x}} \frac{y^2}{x} = \lim_{x\to0} \frac{x}{x} = 1.$$

By particular modes of approach of the point (x, y) to $(0, 0)$,
different limits are possible. This means that no unique limit
exists and emphasizes the fact that, when

$$\lim_{(x,y)\to(a,b)} f(x,y)$$

exists, it is independent of the manner in which (x, y) "approaches"
(a, b).

A pitfall to be avoided in finding the limit of a function of two
variables is that of allowing one variable to approach its limit
first and then the other variable to approach its limit. It is sometimes possible to arrive at an *iterated* limit in this way even when
the limit of the function does not exist. Thus, for example,

$$\lim_{y\to0} \left(\lim_{x\to0} \frac{2x + 3y}{x + y} \right) = \lim_{y\to0} \frac{3y}{y} = 3$$

and

$$\lim_{x\to0} \left(\lim_{y\to0} \frac{2x + 3y}{x + y} \right) = \lim_{x\to0} \frac{2x}{x} = 2.$$

The fact that these two iterated limits are different is a sufficient
proof that

$$\lim_{(x,y)\to(0,0)} \frac{2x + 3y}{x + y}$$

does not exist. It can be shown that, by allowing (x, y) to approach $(0, 0)$ while confined to a straight line through $(0, 0)$, the function can be made to approach any arbitrarily assigned limit.

Answers and Suggestions

CHAPTER II

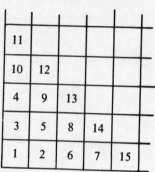

Figure 1

Page 8

3. The diagram suggests a plan for counting the squares. This method can be extended to the exercises 4, 5, and 6.

Page 11

2. Since the set of positive integers is countable, the subset of nonsquare integers is countable and hence the set of positive square roots of these is also countable.

3. The set of squares of the real numbers is equivalent to the set of nonnegative real numbers, which is not countable.

Page 15

1. (i) $\{0, 1, 2\}$, (ii) $\{0, 1\}$, (iii) $\{1, \frac{1}{2}, \frac{1}{3}, \ldots, \frac{1}{10}\}$.
2. (i) $\{-5, -4, -3, -2, -1, 0, 1, 2, 3, 4, 5\}$, (ii) $\{-2, -1, 2, 3\}$, (iii) $\{4, 9, 16, 25, 36, 49\}$.
3. A total of 16 subsets, consisting of the empty set, 4 sets of one each, 6 sets of two each, 4 sets of three each, and one set of four.
4. 64.
5. $2 \leqq x < 7$ or $[2, 7)$, the latter not often used.

8. If $b \in A$ and $b \neq a$, consider a neighborhood of a consisting of points x such that $|x - a| < |b - a|$. This neighborhood contains a point of A different from a and nearer to a than is b. Call this point b_1. Repeat the reasoning with b_1 replacing b. Repeat again, and so on.

Page 25

1. (a) $0 < y < 4$, (b) $-1 \leq y \leq 27$, (c) $\frac{8}{3} < y < 4$, (d) $0 \leq y \leq 4$, (e) $-1 \leq y \leq 1$.

6. In successive intervals, the function is defined by x, $2 - x$, $-2 + x$, $4 - x$, $-4 + x$, $6 - x$, $-6 + x$, $8 - x$.

7. (a) Domain: all real numbers; Range: all nonnegative real numbers; (b) Domain: all real numbers; Range: all negative or zero real numbers; (c) Domain: $1 \leq x \leq 3$; Range: $0 \leq y \leq 1$; (d) Domain: all real numbers; Range: $-1 \leq y \leq 1$.

8. Each of the lines $y = 0$ and $y = 1$ contains a dense set of points that belong to the function and a dense set of points that do not belong. Hence no graph drawn with a pencil can represent the function.

10. $y = \sqrt{r^2 - (x - a)^2}$ and $y = -\sqrt{r^2 - (x - a)^2}$.

11. $\sin(3\pi x)$; $\cos(8x/3)$

12. For $\tan x$ and $\sec x$, exclude all multiples of $\pi/2$ by an odd integer; for $\csc x$ exclude all multiples of π.

13. Rational: (a), (b), (d), (f); Polynomials: (b), (f).

CHAPTER III

Page 39

1. (a) $0, 0, 2, 6, 12$; (b) $\frac{1}{5}, \frac{5}{8}, \frac{9}{11}, \frac{13}{14}, 1$; (c) $0, 2, 0, 2, 0$;
(d) $2, \frac{9}{4}, \frac{64}{27}, \frac{625}{256}, \frac{7776}{3125}$; (e) $2, 1, \frac{8}{9}, 1, \frac{32}{25}$; (f) $1, 0, -1, 0, 1$.

2. The sequences in (a) and (c) $\rightarrow$ limits; that in (d) $\rightarrow \infty$; those in (b) and (e) do neither.

3. (a) is monotone.   4. $m = 10\,000$.   5. $m = 374$.   6. $m = 15$.

7. The smallest integer greater than $\frac{1}{3}\left(\frac{1}{\epsilon} - 1\right)$.

8. $m = 45$.   9. $\frac{3}{5}$.   10. 0.

11. Show, after subtraction, that

$$\frac{a_1 + \ldots + a_n + a_{n+1}}{n + 1} - \frac{a_1 + \ldots + a_n}{n} > 0.$$

14. Begin by summing the progression in the numerator.
15. Begin with the fact that the sequence $(a_n - h) \to 0$.

CHAPTER IV

Page 53

2. 1.   3. 4.   4. 2.   5. 8.
6. 0.   7. 1.   8. $\delta = 0.0014$.   10. Take $\delta = \epsilon/|m|$.
11. (i) $\dfrac{\epsilon}{2 + \epsilon}$, (ii) $\dfrac{2\epsilon}{1 + \epsilon}$. 13. The limit $= 0$.

Page 65   /A

1. (i) 6, (ii) 10 000, (iii) 1, (iv) 2.
7. -2.   8. 2.   9. 0.   10. It increases without limit.
11. (i) It $\to -\infty$, (ii) It $\to +\infty$, (iii) It $\to +\infty$, (iv) It $\to -\infty$.
12. (i) It $\to -\infty$, (ii) It $\to +\infty$.

Page 66   /B

13. Removable discontinuity at $x = 0$; infinite discontinuity at $x = -3$.
14. The functions agree except at $x = 1$, where the first has the value 0 and the second is undefined. Yes.
15. (i) a_n/b_n, (ii) a_0/b_0.
19. For n any integer < 4; For $n = 3$; For $n > 3$.

CHAPTER V

Page 82

1. Convergent. 2. Divergent.   3. Divergent. 4. Convergent.
5. Convergent. 6. Divergent.   7. Divergent. 8. Divergent.
9. Convergent. 10. Divergent.

Page 88

1. Convergent.   2. Convergent.   3. Divergent.   4. Divergent.
5. Convergent.   6. Divergent.   7. Divergent.   8. Convergent.
9. Divergent.   10. Convergent.   11. Divergent.   12. Convergent.
14. Only if $\lim a_n \neq 0$ or is nonexistent, in which cases the series is divergent.

CHAPTER VI

Page 96

1. Slope $= 3x^2$.   3. $2r$; $10x$; $2kt$.   4. 3; 0.

Page 106   /A

2. (a) $15x^2 - 12x + 4$, (b) $2n\, r^{2n-1} - 3n\, r^{n-1}$, (c) $4t(t^2 - 5)$.
4. (a) $10x^4 + 20x^3 - 12x - 15$, (b) $16x^3 + 18x^2 - 18x + 27$.
6. (a) $4r(r^2 - 4)$, (b) $4(5 + 6t - t^2)(3 - t)$.
7. $3u^2 D_x u$.   8. $nu^{n-1} D_x u$.   10. (a) $-2/3$, (b) 3.

Page 107   /B

11. (a) $(-2, 100/3)$, (b) $(4, -8/3)$
12. (a) -13 in./min., (b) -6 in./min./min.; Receding.
14. 60 yd. by 30 yd.   15. Height $=$ diameter.
16. Height: side of base $= 3:4$.   17. 24π sq in./in.
18. 12 in. by 12 in. by 24 in.   19. $(4/3, 4\sqrt{2}/3)$ and
20. $2\sqrt{6}$ units. $(4/3, -4\sqrt{2}/3)$.

CHAPTER VII

Page 125   /A

1. The measure of the length of the interval, $b - a$.
2. 50.   3. 8/3.   4. 21/2.
5. 0.   6. 110.   7. 32/3 sq. units.
8. 6.   9. 16/3.   10. 62/5.

Page 126   /B

11. $f(m) - f(k)$.   12. $-1/12$, $17/12$.   15. $128\pi/7$.

16. $2\pi/5$.   17. $\displaystyle\int_{-3}^{0} 2^x \, dx$.   18. $52/3$.

Index

Printed in the United States of America